*Literature & Thought*

# MYSTERIOUS CIRCUMSTANCES

Perfection Learning

| EDITORIAL DIRECTOR | Julie A. Schumacher |
| --- | --- |
| SENIOR EDITOR | Terry Ofner |
| EDITOR | Sherrie Voss Matthews |
| PERMISSIONS | Laura Pieper |
| REVIEWER | Ann L. Tharnish |

DESIGN AND PHOTO RESEARCH   William Seabright and Associates, Wilmette, Illinois

COVER ART   VOICE I 1963  George Tooker

ACKNOWLEDGMENTS

"The Adventure of the Egyptian Tomb" by Agatha Christie. Reprinted by permission of Harold Ober Associates Incorporated. Copyright © 1924 by Agatha Christie.

"After Agatha Christie," copyright © 1975 by Linda Pastan, from *Carnival Evening: New and Selected Poems 1968-1998* by Linda Pastan. Reprinted by permission of W. W. Norton & Company, Inc.

"Arsenic and Old Rough and Ready" from *Dead Men Do Tell Tales* by William R. Maples. Copyright © 1994 by William R. Maples. Used by permission of Doubleday, a division of Random House, Inc.

"Crop Circles" taken from *Unexplained!*. Edited by Jerome Clark & Nancy Pear. Copyright © 1997 Visible Ink Press. All rights reserved. Reproduced by permission of Gale Research.

"Dreams" by Betsy Hearne. Reprinted with the permission of Margaret K. McElderry Books, an imprint of Simon & Schuster Children's Publishing Division from *Polaroid and Other Poems of View* by Betsy Hearne. Text copyright © 1991 Betsy Hearne.     CONTINUED ON PAGE 144

Paperback ISBN: 0-7891-5051-4
Cover Craft ® ISBN: 0-7807-9022-7

# WHY ARE WE FASCINATED BY MYSTERY?

The question above is the *essential question* that you will consider as you read this book. The literature, activities, and organization of the book will lead you to think critically about this question, to understand the elements of mystery writing, and, perhaps, to become one of the millions of avid mystery readers around the world.

To help you shape your answer to the broad essential question, you will read and respond to four sections, or clusters. Each cluster addresses a specific question and thinking skill.

**CLUSTER ONE** What makes a mystery? **DEFINE**

**CLUSTER TWO** Whodunit? **INVESTIGATE**

**CLUSTER THREE** How do you solve a mystery? **USE LOGIC**

**CLUSTER FOUR** Thinking on your own **SYNTHESIZE**

Notice that the final cluster asks you to think independently about your answer to the essential question—*Why are we fascinated by mystery?*

MOON AND WALL ENCRUSTATIONS
1964 Minor White

# MYSTERIOUS

## DREAMS

During our sleep ghosts walk,

blank-eyed, arms out,

stumbling one on the other,

dropping over hour rims,

reappearing, till light

reseals their eyes and sends

them back, unkempt,

down dimlit corridors of the mind.

BETSY HEARNE

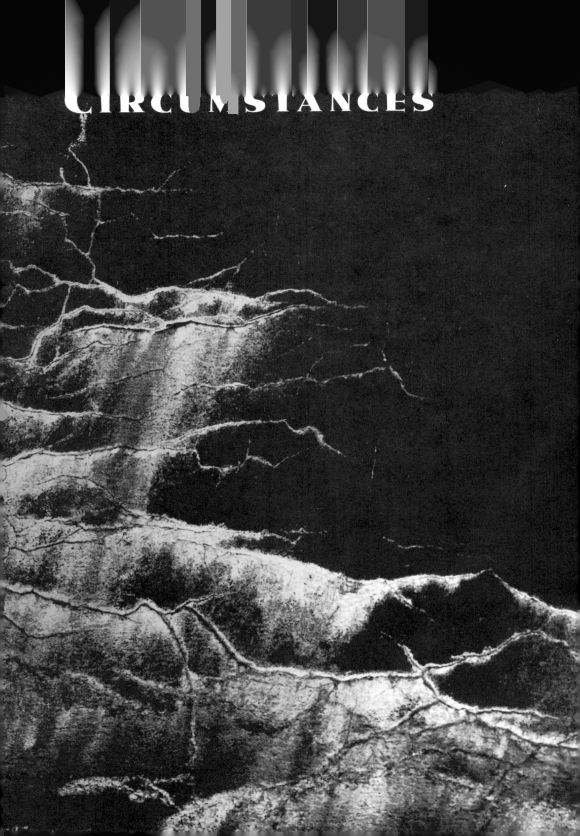

# CIRCUMSTANCES

# TABLE OF CONTENTS

# THE ROOTS OF MYSTERY

There once was a man named Oedipus, the king of the city of Thebes. When a plague struck the city, Oedipus asked a fortune teller how to stop it. He learned that a murderer was in Thebes, and that the plague would continue until the criminal was caught. Oedipus was something of an amateur sleuth who loved solving riddles, so he set to work finding the murderer. He uncovered one clue after another until he learned the horrible truth. He himself was the killer!

Sophocles' tragedy *Oedipus the King*, written between 430 and 425 B.C., might be called the world's oldest murder mystery. Indeed, as plot twists go, its ending rivals the best detective fiction. On the other hand, purists might insist that it isn't quite the real item. After all, Sophocles' audience already knew the identity of the killer from myths and legends. So where was the mystery?

In any case, few if any true mysteries were written for over two thousand years afterward. It wasn't until the early nineteenth century that authors brought the genre into its own. English author Charles Dickens (1812-1870) played a great role in this process. Because Dickens' novels first appeared in magazine installments, he found that a touch of mystery helped keep his readers eager to buy magazines. In his novel *The Mystery of Edwin Drood*, for example, the title character unaccountably disappears. Unfortunately, Dickens died before completing the book, and fans have been trying to solve Drood's disappearance ever since.

Dickens' friend Wilkie Collins (1824-1889) did even more to develop the mystery in novels like *Moonstone,* which deals with the theft of a precious diamond. The plot presents several plausible suspects, but the puzzle is finally cracked by Sergeant Cuff, one of the first detectives in English literature.

While Dickens and Collins pioneered the detective story in England, Edgar Allan Poe (1809-1849) did so in America. Although most famous today for tales of horror and the supernatural, Poe also wrote stories of crime and detection. Some of these featured Parisian detective C. Auguste Dupin. Dupin is not only a great finder of clues but a keen student of human nature. In "The Purloined Letter," Dupin finds a hidden letter by putting himself in the mind of the villain.

Arthur Conan Doyle (1859-1930) acknowledged his debt to Poe when he created the most famous detective ever, Sherlock Holmes. In tales like "The

Mystery of the Speckled Band" and "A Scandal in Bohemia," Holmes shows uncanny intelligence and powers of observation—particularly in comparison with his more average sidekick, the loyal Dr. Watson.

Doyle lived to see the arrival of the "Golden Age" of the mystery, which began around 1920 and lasted until around 1945. Among the great writers of this period were Agatha Christie (1890-1976) and Dorothy L. Sayers (1893-1957). Christie's amateur sleuths Hercule Poirot and Miss Jane Marple display their prowess in novels like *Murder on the Orient Express* and *The Mirror Crack'd*. Sayers' Lord Peter Wimsey performed feats of detection in novels like *Whose Body?* and *The Nine Tailors*.

The mysteries of Christie, Sayers, and their followers feature intricate puzzles solved by clever amateur sleuths; they are seldom shockingly violent. For this reason, they are sometimes called "cozies." Some American authors disliked "cozy" mystery writing and rebelled with "hard-boiled" stories, which portrayed crime in a grim, realistic way.

In novels like *The Maltese Falcon*, Dashiell Hammett (1894-1961) introduced the hard-boiled private eye Sam Spade. Likewise, Raymond Chandler (1888-1959) presented the tough but vulnerable detective Philip Marlowe in novels like *The Big Sleep*. Mickey Spillane (1918- ) continued the hard-boiled tradition with stories of detective Mike Hammer. Even Spillane's titles, including *Kiss Me, Deadly* and *Tomorrow I Die*, have a hard-boiled flavor.

Today's fans are still somewhat divided into "cozy" and "hard-boiled" camps, but mysteries have become too diverse to be tucked into simple categories. And of course, the genre has undergone many changes. For example, feminism has brought female detectives to the fore, even in hard-boiled fiction.

Television has also brought many changes, playing a special role in bringing the mystery to an ever-wider audience. One of the most popular television detectives is Lieutenant Columbo, who first appeared on NBC in 1971. *Columbo* brought a new twist to an old formula. Each episode began with the murder itself, so viewers knew right away who the killer was. Fans found plenty of thrills in watching Columbo solve a seemingly unsolvable crime.

So in looking back, perhaps *Oedipus the King* is the real item after all. Indeed, it might even be said to be thousands of years ahead of its time—the true pattern for all mysteries since. A crime, a sleuth, and a solution: these have always been the essential ingredients for a mystery, and doubtless always will be.

# CONCEPT VOCABULARY

*You will find the following terms and definitions useful as you read and discuss the selections in this book.*

**alibi**  an excuse used to avoid blame or punishment

**cat burglar**  a burglar who is able to break into a building without being noticed

**cozy mystery**  a mystery involving a close group of people who would not normally be party to a crime. Many of Agatha Christie's Hercule Poirot and Miss Marple mysteries are examples of this type of story.

**deduction**  a conclusion reached by logical thinking

**embezzlement**  to steal money or property entrusted to one's care

**evidence**  something that furnishes proof

**felony**  a serious crime punishable by imprisonment

**forensic science**  scientific examination of evidence for use in a criminal case; the study of scientific evidence found on a dead body or at a crime scene

**hard-boiled mystery**  a detective story featuring a tough, unsentimental detective who has a matter-of-fact attitude toward violence. Kinsey Milhone, Sam Spade, V.I. Warshawski, and Mike Hammer are examples of hard-boiled detectives.

**locked-room mystery**  a mystery in which a seemingly impossible crime is committed; for example, a crime occurs in a room that apparently allows no entrance or exit for the criminal.

**private eye**  another name for a private investigator, a person who is licensed to perform detective work but who is not a part of a police force

**red herring**  a clue or detail that draws attention away from the criminal

**sleuth**  a detective

**stool pigeon**  an informer or spy

**suspect**  a person suspected of committing a crime

**thriller**  a mystery designed to hold a reader's interest through intrigue and suspense. Stephen King and R.L Stine write thriller mysteries.

**whodunit**  a mystery or detective story

**witness**  a person who offers evidence about a crime and/or is called on to testify in court

# CLUSTER ONE

## What Makes A Mystery?
### Thinking Skill   DEFINING

# The Framing Game

PAUL BISHOP

**G**o on, Tommy. Take 'em!"

"No way, man. We're gonna get caught."

"How? Nobody's looking. Just put 'em on and take 'em."

"If it's that easy, you do it."

"Hey, I'm ready," Spider said, pointing at the new pair of Air Jordans that he had just taken off the store shelf and put on his feet. "But you need the new vrooooms more than me. Look at those things you're wearing."

Tommy Norman looked down at his worn-out canvas high-tops.

Spider nudged him with his elbow. "The only way you're gonna score any hoops against Mansfield in those things is because everyone'll be laughing so hard."

"I don't know." Tommy shook his head. "It ain't right."

"Man, don't be such a wuss," Spider said. "You think the store's gonna miss a couple of pair of shoes? Just put 'em on your feet and run."

Tommy examined the flashy pair of high-top Air Jordans in his hands. It was as if they had "high-scorer" written all over them. A tiny orange basketball on the side of each shoe acted as a pump to tighten the leather around the foot. Tommy figured that feature alone was worth an extra ten points a game.

The shoes would be like magic. They would make him fly down the court, slash through defenses, and slam-dunk with ease. He was already the top scorer in the toughest high-school league in the Los Angeles area, but these babies would make him an even bigger star. College scouts from all over were going to be in the stands for Friday's league championship game, and Tommy wanted to be sure he made an impression.

The game was going to be a monster bash. Tommy and his Franklin High teammates against their crosstown rival, Mansfield. The game was so big that it was going to be played in the Great Western Forum, the home court of the Los Angeles Lakers.

The game was still two days away, but the two boys were already feeling the jitters.

Tommy fingered the price tag. One hundred and twenty-eight bucks. No way did he have that kind of money, and his mom certainly wasn't going to cough up that many dead presidents just so he could score more points on the basketball court. She had too many other things to worry about—like paying the rent.

Spider Thompson was grinning at him, wriggling in anticipation. "You gonna be one awesome dude with them wings on your feet. Even Dolbert won't be able to slow you down."

Tommy's heart jumped. Eddie Dolbert was Mansfield's starting center and had been all-conference for the past three years. He was big, tough, and aggressive and controlled the key like King Kong.

"You really think these will help me against Dolbert?"

"Man, I know so. You gonna be like a hot wind. And all you gotta do to own 'em is put 'em on, blast past the cash registers, and keep running."

Tommy looked around again. Anything you could possibly want for any sport was somewhere on the Sports Depot's shelves. The shoe section stocked every brand and every style imaginable. Under each style were boxes in different sizes on help-yourself racks. You tried the shoes on and, if they fit, took them up to a register to pay for them—unless you were planning to steal them.

A Sports Depot employee suddenly appeared out of nowhere. "You guys need help?" he asked.

Tommy's heart jumped. "N-n-n-no thanks," he stammered.

The employee took a hard look at both boys before moving away.

"Oh, man," whined Tommy. "That guy figures we're up to something."

"Be cool," Spider said, urgently. "He don't know squat."

"Man, his eyes were all over us," Tommy said, watching the corner where the employee had disappeared. "It was like he knew us or something."

"That's 'cause everybody knows us," Spider said. "We be stylin' on the basketball court and everybody knows we gonna blow the Mansfield team off the court."

"No, man. I know that guy from somewhere, and he spells trouble."

"You're crazy, dude. The only thing that guy can spell is words of three letters or less. If he's such big-time trouble, how come he's working in a square joint like this?"

"I don't know, but I still have a feeling he's bad news."

"Man, you are such a chicken. Are you gonna pick yourself up a new pair of scoots or not? Make up your mind 'cause I'm outta here."

"Wait!" Tommy said, but it was too late. Spider was off and running toward the registers.

With the Air Jordans still in his hands, Tommy followed his teammate out of the shoe section.

▲　▲　▲

The next morning on the school bus, Tommy did not sit with Spider like normal. Spider was at the front of the bus being cool and showing off his new shoes. Tommy sat in the back.

As the bus turned the corner, Tommy could see a huge crowd of kids gathered in front of Franklin High's main entrance. They were upset and it was easy to see why.

During the night somebody had used green and white spray paint on the front doors, walls, and windows. Green and white—the colors of Mansfield High. In several spots Tommy even saw the letters MJAM, the signature of a tagging crew known as the Mansfield Jammers, in green spray paint.

When Tommy stepped off the bus, Coach Jackson and Mr. Smithson, Franklin High School's dean of discipline, were waiting on the sidewalk. Coach Jackson was holding on to the arm of a scared-looking Spider and called Tommy over as soon as he spotted him.

"What's going on?" Tommy asked as he reached Spider's side.

Coach Jackson sighed. "Tommy, I'm very disappointed in you."

"What are you talking about, Coach? Everybody on the team has been real low-key about the rivalry—just like you asked us—This isn't our fault."

"I'm not talking about the graffiti," Coach Jackson said. "I want you in Smithson's office, right now."

As the two boys were escorted through the school's entrance in front of almost the entire student body, Tommy's mind was in a whirl. He hadn't done anything wrong. He couldn't believe he was in trouble.

Once in his office, Mr. Smithson took his place behind his large metal desk. Tommy and Spider sat facing him. Coach Jackson leaned against the closed door of the office as if he expected the boys to make a sudden break for freedom.

Mr. Smithson leaned forward. "Those are pretty fancy shoes you're wearing, Spider. Where did you get them?"

Tommy felt the blood drain out of his face. How could Mr. Smithson know about the shoes Spider snatched?

"I bought them," Spider said. His voice cracked with the lie.

"No, you stole them," Mr. Smithson said calmly, "from the Sports Depot."

Spider looked at Tommy angrily.

"Hey, I didn't say anything," Tommy said defensively.

"No, you certainly didn't," Mr. Smithson said. "Because then you would have to explain these—" From under his desk, he brought out the Air Jordans Tommy had been holding in the Sports Depot.

Tommy looked confused. "Where did those come from?"

"Don't play stupid, Tommy," Coach Jackson said. "We found them in your gym locker."

"But—" Tommy started to defend himself. Mr. Smithson cut him off with a raised hand.

"Don't dig yourself in deeper by lying. The evidence is clear." Mr. Smithson swiveled around in his chair and turned on a television set and a VCR that sat on the shelf behind the desk. He pressed the play button on the VCR's remote control.

A grainy, black-and-white tape began to play on the television screen.

"This is the security tape that was made at the Sports Depot yesterday. Every ten seconds it changes to a camera in a different part of the store."

Tommy and Spider watched the tape in silence. After a few seconds they could see themselves standing in the shoe section of the store. Spider was putting a pair of shoes on his feet and Tommy was holding a pair in his hands. The tape moved off to show ten-second snippets of the camping section, the cash registers, and other parts of the store. After about a minute, it again showed Tommy and Spider in the shoe section. Tommy still had the shoes in his hands, and Spider was waving his arms around talking to him.

The next time the tape showed the shoe section, the Sports Depot employee who had surprised them was standing with the two boys. The tape moved away to the camping section. When the tape moved on to the cash registers, it showed Spider running out the front door. Just before the tape moved on again, it showed Tommy's head and shoulders as he followed Spider.

"This tape and the shoes on Spider's feet," Mr. Smithson said, "leave me with little doubt that the shoes found in Tommy's locker are stolen property." He pointed at the pair of beautiful new Air Jordans that sat on his desk like prisoners before a judge.

"But—" Tommy tried again.

"I don't want to hear it," Mr. Smithson said, interrupting.

"Tommy didn't steal—" Spider started, but he too was cut off.

"Spider, unless you can show me a receipt for those shoes, I don't want to hear any more out of you. Take them off now and put them on my desk."

Spider hesitated only for a moment.

"I think both of you boys should consider yourselves lucky. Sports Depot has said that they will not press charges with the police as long as the shoes are returned. But I don't believe we can let things go without some form of punishment."

Tommy and Spider looked at each other.

"As of this moment," Mr. Smithson continued, "you are both suspended from the basketball team."

"Hey! Wait a minute," Tommy stood up as if someone had lit a fire under his seat. "That's not fair. I didn't steal those shoes."

"Are you denying you were in the Sports Depot?"

"No, but—"

"Are you denying these are the shoes you had in your hands on the tape?"

"No, but—"

"Are you calling Coach Jackson and myself liars when we say we found these shoes in your gym locker?"

"No, but—"

"Then I don't think there's anything further to talk about."

"Coach?" Tommy pleaded. He was on the verge of tears. This could ruin everything—the league championship, his scholarship chances—everything.

"I'm sorry, Tommy. There's nothing I can do. You made your choices. Now you have to live with them." Coach Jackson's eyes were as cold as two dead fish. "And so do the rest of us. You not only let yourself down, you let the team down."

"But I didn't, Coach. I didn't steal those shoes."

"Then how did they get in your gym locker?"

"I don't know." Tommy couldn't think, and he couldn't trust himself to say anything more.

▲   ▲   ▲

"It's not fair," Spider said. He and Tommy were sitting alone at a lunch table.

"Shut up," said Tommy. He couldn't remember anything that had happened in class all morning. All he could think about was being suspended from the basketball team for something he didn't do.

"Man, I couldn't believe Coach Jackson. And that jerk Smithson wouldn't listen to nothing."

"Just shut up," Tommy repeated. "Would you have listened to us? Anyway, you stole the shoes, so you don't have anything to cry about."

"It's not like you weren't thinking about it."

"Right. But the fact is, I didn't steal 'em. So, somebody else put 'em in my locker."

"What are you gonna do about it?"

"I'm gonna find out who did."

Tommy looked around the lunch area. Even here, the vandals had managed to spray paint the walls, and Tommy noticed the MJAM tag signed across one of the lunch tables. He looked away, and then back again.

"Wait a minute," he said to Spider. "The Jammers."

"Yeah? So what?" asked Spider.

"The Jammers, man. The Jammers," Tommy said, sounding excited.

Spider looked confused. "Like I said, so what? Everybody knows they're the only ones who would do something like this. I bet the cops are all over them already."

"Yeah, but you can bet they're clean by now—dumped all the paint cans. And the crew ain't gonna split on each other. They'll walk like they always do."

Spider shrugged. "So what are you getting so excited about?"

"Think, man. Who runs the Jammers?"

"Jammer Dolbert," Spider said without hesitation, "Eddie Dolbert's older brother."

"Now think about yesterday at the Sports Depot. . . ."

Spider looked confused again.

"The guy," Tommy insisted.

"What guy?"

"The guy who almost caught us stealing the shoes."

"Too cool," Spider said as he suddenly understood. "That was Jammer Dolbert!"

"Yeah, yeah!" said Tommy. "I almost didn't recognize him with his hair mowed down and wearing straight clothes, but that was him."

Jammer was a year older than his basketball-playing brother, and as different from him as night is from day. Eddie Dolbert was a tough guy on the basketball court, but he had worked hard to hone his skills and deserved his reputation. Jammer was a different story. Tommy was surprised that Jammer was even working a legitimate job.

"You think he was planning all this when we saw him?" Spider asked, waving a hand at the vandalism.

"Not just this," Tommy said, "but maybe something else as well."

▲   ▲   ▲

Later that afternoon, Tommy knocked on the door to Coach Jackson's office.

"Come in."

Tommy opened the door and stuck his head around. "I'm sorry to bother you, Coach," he said, gathering up his courage, "but could I please ask you a question?"

Coach Jackson looked at his star center. "What is it?" The coach's voice was flat and calm.

"I wanted to know how you got into my locker today."

Coach Jackson gave Tommy a hard look before answering. "We cut the lock off."

"Do you still have it?"

Coach Jackson pointed to a lump of metal on his desk. The shackle had been cut through on one side.

Tommy took a key out of his pocket. He picked up the lock and examined it. "This isn't my lock, Coach. Mine was a Master Lock." Tommy held up his key. "This one is a Wesloc." He inserted the key into the lock, but it didn't turn.

Coach Jackson raised his eyebrows. "You could have simply brought in a different key."

"I could have, but I didn't," Tommy said defiantly. "I'm telling you I didn't steal those shoes. I thought about it, but I didn't steal 'em."

Coach Jackson shrugged. "You're going to have to do better than that if you expect to convince Mr. Smithson."

"Oh, I'll do better," Tommy said. "But can you please tell me why you checked my locker for the shoes?" Tommy was trying hard to talk polite like his mother had taught him. He needed to get Coach Jackson on his side.

The coach hesitated, then answered. "The security tape was brought to the school this morning by one of the Sports Depot employees. He told us the manager of the store asked that we look at the tape and then check your locker to see if you had hidden the shoes there."

"Did he ask you to check Spider's locker?"

"No," Coach Jackson said thoughtfully. "When we viewed the tape, of course, we recognized Spider. After finding the shoes in your locker, we didn't have time before the buses arrived to check any further. We waited for you and Spider and it was obvious that Spider was wearing the stolen shoes when he came off the bus."

Tommy nodded. "Well," he said, still trying to talk polite, "I called the Sports Depot manager and asked him what they do about guys they catch ripping them off. He said the store always calls the cops."

Coach Jackson continued to look unimpressed, but Tommy was sure his argument was working.

"Spider stole the pair of shoes he was wearing when he ran out of the store," Tommy said. "But that tape just shows my back. You don't get a look at my feet. I was wearing my regular high-tops, not those Air Jordans you found in my locker. I tossed 'em before I left the store. I didn't want to steal 'em. I knew it was wrong."

Coach Jackson shook his head. "Well, if you didn't steal them, then who did? And how did they get in your locker?"

"I think I know. All I have to do now is prove it."

▲   ▲   ▲

Despite Spider's taunting words when they had been in the Sports Depot, Tommy didn't think of himself as a chicken. Still, as he waited in the parking lot of Mansfield High for school to let out, his stomach hurt with tension. He was in enemy territory, and he knew if he didn't play things right he could end up getting thumped on.

The school bell rang and students started to empty out of buildings. Several people spotted Tommy in his Franklin High letterman's jacket as he leaned against the bumper of Eddie Dolbert's Toyota truck, but they left him alone. Still, Tommy felt their eyes on him. Maybe he shouldn't have come. Maybe this whole thing was a real bad idea. He felt himself start to sweat.

He was about to change his mind about sticking around when Eddie Dolbert and two of his buddies saw him by the truck and walked deliberately toward him.

"Are you crazy, coming here?" Dolbert asked Tommy when he was close enough. "Get off my truck."

Tommy straightened up. He hoped Eddie and his buddies couldn't see his knees shaking inside his jeans.

"We heard you got yourself bounced off the team," Eddie said.

"Bad news travels fast," Tommy replied.

"Good news for us," said one of Dolbert's buddies.

"We don't like thieves at Mansfield," Eddie said.

"I'm not a thief."

"Oh, yeah. So how come you got bounced?" Eddie asked.

"Because your brother, Jammer, set me up," Tommy said, "at the same time he and his crew vandalized Franklin last night."

Eddie's buddies started to move threateningly toward Tommy. *Here it comes,* Tommy thought.

"Wait a minute," Eddie said. Everyone stopped, and Tommy started to breathe again. "What makes you think my brother is behind this?"

"Come on," Tommy said. "If you didn't know he was behind half the petty trouble around here you wouldn't be asking me that question."

When Eddie didn't say anything, Tommy continued. "Jammer works at Sports Depot, right?"

Eddie nodded.

"He saw me with Spider when Spider took the shoes. He also probably saw me dump the pair I was carrying. He knew I didn't steal 'em, but when he looked at the security videotape, it showed me running out after Spider, but the tape changed to another part of the store before my feet came into the picture. Jammer saw that as a chance to frame me and get me out of Friday's game."

Eddie still didn't look totally convinced. "How do you figure he framed you?"

"He must have snuck that pair of shoes out of the store when he got off work. Then, when he and his crew hit the school last night, I figure he broke into the locker room, cut the lock off of my locker, put the shoes inside, and put his own lock back on. Then he sent the security tape to Mr. Smithson this morning and asked him to check my locker for the shoes as if he was representing the Sports Depot."

"How did he know which locker was yours?"

"Our names are on them, just like yours are here."

Eddie nodded.

Tommy stood looking at Dolbert. "So," he said eventually, "do you want to play this game tomorrow on even terms and let the best team win? Or do want your brother to have handed you the game on a platter?"

"I ain't afraid of taking you on," Dolbert said.

▲   ▲   ▲

It was Friday night and the Forum was packed. Tommy was tying the frayed laces on his canvas high-tops and trying to stay calm. He had only gotten word that he would be allowed to play at the end of seventh period, when school let out.

As he stood up, Tommy spotted Spider leaning against his locker. Spider wasn't supposed to be in the locker room, but he had snuck in to talk to Tommy.

"Man, I wish I was going out there with you," Spider said.

"Me too," Tommy told him. "But—"

"I know, I know," Spider interrupted. "I screwed up. But at least the cops nailed Jammer for framing you. How did they know?"

"They found green and white spray-paint cans when they searched his car and then took it from there."

"I can't believe Jammer was stupid enough to keep the paint cans he used," Spider said.

"He wasn't," Tommy told him with a sly smile.

"What do you mean?"

"Well, two can play at the framing game. Eddie Dolbert didn't want to walk off with this game and have everyone say Mansfield was just lucky because you and I weren't playing. So, he gave me the spare key to his brother's car. I put the cans in the car while Jammer was at work. Then I called the cops and tipped 'em off."

"Oh, man," said Spider. "That was really sly."

"After they got the spray cans and started questioning Jammer, he rolled over and told them the whole story. Of course it helped that Eddie talked to his brother and made him come clean about the shoes."

"And Smithson bought off on it?"

"He didn't have much choice," Tommy said. "He talked to the Sports Depot's manager and confirmed they didn't send the tape over here. It was Jammer himself who brought the tape over and gave it to Mr.

Smithson. The Sports Depot manager also said that Jammer had been suspected of stealing from the store for a while now, but just hadn't been caught."

"Now that's what I call fighting fire with fire," Spider said.

Coach Jackson gave the team the word to head out to the court for warm-ups. He slapped Tommy on the shoulders as he moved by.

"You're going to smoke 'em tonight, kid," he said.

A moment later Tommy stepped onto the court and looked over at Dolbert. The tall, heavily muscled Mansfield center ignored him.

Yeah, he was going to smoke 'em tonight, all right. And he wasn't going to need a pair of fancy basketball shoes to do it. ∾

# The Adventure of the Egyptian Tomb

AGATHA CHRISTIE

I have always considered that one of the most thrilling and dramatic of the many adventures I have shared with Poirot was that of our investigation into the strange series of deaths which followed upon the discovery and opening of the Tomb of King Men-her-Ra.

Hard upon the discovery of the Tomb of Tutankh-Amen by Lord Carnarvon, Sir John Willard and Mr. Bleibner of New York, pursuing their excavations not far from Cairo, in the vicinity of the Pyramids of Gizeh,[1] came unexpectedly on a series of funeral chambers. The greatest interest was aroused by their discovery. The Tomb appeared to be that of King Men-her-Ra, one of those shadowy kings of the Eighth Dynasty, when the Old Kingdom was falling to decay. Little was known about this period, and the discoveries were fully reported in the newspapers.

An event soon occurred which took a profound hold on the public mind. Sir John Willard died quite suddenly of heart failure.

The more sensational newspapers immediately took the opportunity of reviving all the old superstitious stories connected with the ill luck of certain Egyptian treasures. The unlucky Mummy at the British Museum, that hoary old chestnut,[2] was dragged out with fresh zest, was quietly denied by the Museum, but nevertheless enjoyed all its usual vogue.

A fortnight later Mr. Bleibner died of acute blood poisoning, and a few

---

1 **Pyramids of Gizeh:** Tombs of Egyptian kings located near Cairo, Egypt.
2 **hoary old chestnut:** ancient object.

days afterwards a nephew of his shot himself in New York. The "Curse of Men-her-Ra" was the talk of the day, and the magic power of dead-and-gone Egypt was exalted to a fetish point.

It was then that Poirot received a brief note from Lady Willard, widow of the dead archaeologist, asking him to go and see her at her house in Kensington Square. I accompanied him.

Lady Willard was a tall, thin woman, dressed in deep mourning. Her haggard face bore eloquent testimony to her recent grief.

"It is kind of you to have come so promptly, Monsieur Poirot."

"I am at your service, Lady Willard. You wished to consult me?"

"You are, I am aware, a detective, but it is not only as a detective that I wish to consult you. You are a man of original views, I know, you have imagination, experience of the world; tell me, Monsieur Poirot, what are your views on the supernatural?"

Poirot hesitated for a moment before he replied. He seemed to be considering. Finally he said:

Egyptian tomb sculpture.

"Let us not misunderstand each other, Lady Willard. It is not a general question that you are asking me here. It has a personal application, has it not? You are referring obliquely to the death of your late husband?"

"That is so," she admitted.

"You want me to investigate the circumstances of his death?"

"I want you to ascertain for me exactly how much is newspaper chatter, and how much may be said to be founded on fact? Three deaths, Monsieur Poirot—each one explicable taken by itself, but taken together surely an almost unbelievable coincidence, and all within a month of the opening of the tomb! It may be mere superstition, it may be some potent curse from the past that operates in ways undreamed of by modern science. The fact remains—three deaths! And I am afraid, Monsieur Poirot, horribly afraid. It may not yet be the end."

"For whom do you fear?"

"For my son. When the news of my husband's death came I was ill. My son, who has just come down from Oxford, went out there. He brought the—the body home, but now has gone out again, in spite of my prayers and entreaties. He is so fascinated by the work that he intends to take his father's place and carry on the system of excavations. You may think me a foolish, credulous woman, but, Monsieur Poirot, I am afraid. Supposing that the spirit of the dead King is not yet appeased? Perhaps to you I seem to be talking nonsense—"

"No, indeed, Lady Willard," said Poirot quickly. "I, too, believe in the force of superstition, one of the greatest forces the world has ever known."

I looked at him in surprise. I should never have credited Poirot with being superstitious. But the little man was obviously in earnest.

"What you really demand is that I shall protect your son? I will do my utmost to keep him from harm."

"Yes, in the ordinary way, but against an occult influence?"

"In volumes of the Middle Ages, Lady Willard, you will find many ways of counteracting black magic. Perhaps they knew more than we moderns with all our boasted science. Now let us come to facts, that I may have guidance. Your husband had always been a devoted Egyptologist, hadn't he?"

"Yes, from his youth upwards. He was one of the greatest living authorities upon the subject."

"But Mr. Bleibner, I understand, was more or less of an amateur?"

"Oh, quite. He was a very wealthy man who dabbled freely in any subject that happened to take his fancy. My husband managed to interest him in Egyptology, and it was his money that was so useful in financing the expedition."

"And the nephew? What do you know of his tastes? Was he with the party at all?"

"I do not think so. In fact I never knew of his existence till I read of his death in the paper. I do not think he and Mr. Bleibner can have been at all intimate. He never spoke of having any relations."

"Who are the other members of the party?"

"Well, there's Dr. Tosswill, a minor official connected with the British Museum; Mr. Schneider of the Metropolitan Museum in New York; a young American secretary; Dr. Ames, who accompanied the expedition in his professional capacity; and Hassan, my husband's devoted native servant."

"Do you remember the name of the American secretary?"

"Harper, I think, but I cannot be sure. He had not been with Mr. Bleibner very long I know. He was a very pleasant young fellow."

"Thank you, Lady Willard."

"If there is anything else—"

"For the moment, nothing. Leave it now in my hands, and be assured that I will do all that is humanly possible to protect your son."

They were not exactly reassuring words, and I observed Lady Willard wince as he uttered them. Yet, at the same time, the fact that he had not pooh-poohed her fears seemed in itself to be a relief to her. For my part I had never before suspected that Poirot had so deep a vein of superstition in his nature. I tackled him on the subject as we went homeward. His manner was grave and earnest.

"But yes, Hastings. I believe in these things. You must not underrate the force of superstition."

"What are we going to do about it?"

"*Toujours pratique*,[3] the good Hastings! *Eh bien*,[4] to begin with we are going to cable to New York for fuller details of young Mr. Bleibner's death."

He duly sent off his cable. The reply was full and precise. Young Rupert Bleibner had been in low water for several years. He had been a beachcomber and a remittance man[5] in several South Sea islands, but had returned to New York two years ago, where he had rapidly sunk lower

---

3 *Toujours pratique:* always practical.

4 *Eh bien:* oh, well.

5 **remittance man:** repossession man, one who comes to claim items not paid for.

and lower. The most significant thing, to my mind, was that he had recently managed to borrow enough money to take him to Egypt. "I've a good friend there I can borrow from," he had declared. Here, however, his plans had gone awry. He had returned to New York cursing his skin-flint of an uncle who cared more for the bones of dead-and-gone kings than his own flesh and blood. It was during his sojourn in Egypt that the death of Sir John Willard had occurred. Rupert had plunged once more into his life of dissipation in New York and then, without warning, he had committed suicide, leaving behind him a letter which contained some curious phrases. It seemed written in a sudden fit of remorse. He referred to himself as a leper and an outcast, and the letter ended by declaring that such as he were better dead.

A shadowy theory leapt into my brain. I had never really believed in the vengeance of a long dead Egyptian king. I saw here a more modern crime. Supposing this young man had decided to do away with his uncle—preferably by poison. By mistake, Sir John Willard receives the fatal dose. The young man returns to New York, haunted by his crime. The news of his uncle's death reaches him. He realizes how unnecessary his crime has been, and stricken with remorse takes his own life.

I outlined my solution to Poirot. He was interested.

"It is ingenious what you have thought of there—decidedly it is ingenious. It may even be true. But you leave out of count the fatal influence of the Tomb."

I shrugged my shoulders.

"You still think that has something to do with it?"

"So much so, *mon ami*,[6] that we start for Egypt tomorrow."

"What?" I cried, astonished.

"I have said it." An expression of conscious heroism spread over Poirot's face. Then he groaned. "But oh," he lamented, "the sea! The hateful sea!"[7]

▲  ▲  ▲

It was a week later. Beneath our feet was the golden sand of the desert. The hot sun poured down overhead. Poirot, the picture of misery, wilted by my side. The little man was not a good traveler. Our four days' voyage

6 **mon ami:** my friend.
7 Poirot suffers from seasickness and avoids
   traveling by boat whenever possible.

from Marseilles had been one long agony to him. He had landed at Alexandria the wraith[8] of his former self, even his usual neatness had deserted him. We had arrived in Cairo and had driven out at once to the Mena House Hotel, right in the shadow of the Pyramids.

The charm of Egypt had laid hold of me. Not so Poirot. Dressed precisely the same as in London, he carried a small clothes brush in his pocket and waged an unceasing war on the dust which accumulated on his dark apparel.

"And my boots," he wailed. "Regard them, Hastings. My boots, of the neat patent leather, usually so smart and shining. See, the sand is inside them, which is painful, and outside them, which outrages the eyesight. Also the heat, it causes my mustaches to become limp—but limp!"

"Look at the Sphinx," I urged. "Even I can feel the mystery and the charm it exhales."

Poirot looked at it discontentedly.

"It has not the air happy," he declared. "How could it, half-buried in sand in that untidy fashion. Ah, this cursed sand!"

"Come, now, there's a lot of sand in Belgium," I reminded him, mindful of a holiday spent at Knocke-sur-mer in the midst of "*Les dunes impeccables*"[9] as the guidebook had phrased it.

"Not in Brussels," declared Poirot. He gazed at the Pyramids thoughtfully. "It is true that they, at least, are of a shape solid and geometrical but their surface is of an unevenness most unpleasing. And the palm trees, I like them not. Not even do they plant them in rows!"

I cut short his lamentations, by suggesting that we should start for the camp. We were to ride there on camels, and the beasts were patiently kneeling, waiting for us to mount, in charge of several picturesque boys headed by a voluble dragoman.[10]

I pass over the spectacle of Poirot on a camel. He started by groans and lamentations and ended by shrieks, gesticulations and invocations to the Virgin Mary and every Saint in the calendar. In the end, he descended ignominiously and finished the journey on a diminutive donkey. I must admit that a trotting camel is no joke for the amateur. I was stiff for several days.

8 **wraith:** shadow.

9 *Les dunes impeccables:* impeccable sand dunes.

10 **dragoman:** caravan driver.

At last we neared the scene of the excavations. A sunburned man with a gray beard, in white clothes and wearing a helmet, came to meet us.

"Monsieur Poirot and Captain Hastings? We received your cable. I'm sorry that there was no one to meet you in Cairo. An unforeseen event occurred which completely disorganized our plans."

Poirot paled. His hand, which had stolen to his clothes brush, stayed its course.

"Not another death?" he breathed.

"Yes."

"Sir Guy Willard?" I cried.

"No, Captain Hastings. My American colleague, Mr. Schneider."

"And the cause?" demanded Poirot.

"Tetanus."

I blanched. All around me I seemed to feel an atmosphere of evil, subtle and menacing. A horrible thought flashed across me. Supposing I were next?

"*Mon Dieu*," said Poirot, in a very low voice. "I do not understand this. It is horrible. Tell me, monsieur, there is no doubt that it was tetanus?"

Site of pharaoh Tutankhamen's tomb, discovered in 1922 by Howard Carter.

"I believe not. But Dr. Ames will tell you more than I can do."

"Ah, of course, you are not the doctor."

"My name is Tosswill."

This, then, was the British expert described by Lady Willard as being a minor official of the British Museum. There was something at once grave and steadfast about him that took my fancy.

"If you will come with me," continued Dr. Tosswill. "I will take you to Sir Guy Willard. He was most anxious to be informed as soon as you should arrive."

We were taken across the camp to a large tent. Dr. Tosswill lifted up the flap and we entered. Three men were sitting inside.

"Monsieur Poirot and Captain Hastings have arrived, Sir Guy," said Tosswill.

The youngest of the three men jumped up and came forward to greet us. There was a certain impulsiveness in his manner which reminded me of his mother. He was not nearly so sunburned as the others, and that fact, coupled with a certain haggardness around the eyes, made him look older than his twenty-two years. He was clearly endeavoring to bear up under a severe mental strain.

He introduced his two companions, Dr. Ames, a capable-looking man of thirty-odd, with a touch of graying hair at the temples, and Mr. Harper, the secretary, a pleasant, lean young man wearing the national insignia of horn-rimmed spectacles.

After a few minutes' desultory conversation the latter went out, and Dr. Tosswill followed him. We were left alone with Sir Guy and Dr. Ames.

"Please ask any questions you want to ask, Monsieur Poirot," said Willard. "We are utterly dumbfounded at this strange series of disasters, but it isn't—it can't be, anything but coincidence."

There was a nervousness about his manner which rather belied the words. I saw that Poirot was studying him keenly.

"Your heart is really in this work, Sir Guy?"

"Rather. No matter what happens, or what comes of it, the work is going on. Make up your mind to that."

Poirot wheeled around on the other.

"What have you to say to that, *monsieur le docteur*?"

"Well," drawled the doctor, "I'm not for quitting myself."

Poirot made one of those expressive grimaces of his.

"Then, *èvidemment*,[11] we must find out just how we stand. When did Mr. Schneider's death take place?"

"Three days ago."

"You are sure it was tetanus?"

"Dead sure."

"It couldn't have been a case of strychnine poisoning, for instance?"

"No, Monsieur Poirot, I see what you are getting at. But it was a clear case of tetanus."

"Did you not inject antiserum?"

"Certainly we did," said the doctor drily. "Every conceivable thing that could be done was tried."

---

11 *èvidemment:* evidently.

"Had you the antiserum with you?"

"No. We procured it from Cairo."

"Have there been any other cases of tetanus in the camp?"

"No, not one."

"Are you certain that the death of Mr. Bleibner was not due to tetanus?"

"Absolutely plumb certain. He had a scratch upon his thumb which became poisoned, and septicemia[12] set in. It sounds pretty much the same to a layman, I dare say, but the two things are entirely different."

"Then we have four deaths—all totally dissimilar, one heart failure, one blood poisoning, one suicide and one tetanus."

"Exactly, Monsieur Poirot."

"Are you certain that there is nothing which might link the four together?"

"I don't quite understand you?"

"I will put it plainly. Was any act committed by those four men which might seem to denote disrespect to the spirit of Men-her-Ra?"

The doctor gazed at Poirot in astonishment.

"You're talking through your hat, Monsieur Poirot. Surely you've not been guyed into believing all that fool talk?"

"Absolute nonsense," muttered Willard angrily.

Poirot remained placidly immovable, blinking a little out of his green cat's eyes.

"So you do not believe it, *monsieur le docteur*?"

"No, sir, I do not," declared the doctor emphatically. "I am a scientific man, and I believe only what science teaches."

"Was there no science then in Ancient Egypt?" asked Poirot softly. He did not wait for a reply, and indeed Dr. Ames seemed rather at a loss for the moment. "No, no, do not answer me, but tell me this. What do the native workmen think?"

"I guess," said Dr. Ames, "that, where white folk lose their heads, natives aren't going to be far behind. I'll admit that they're getting what you might call scared—but they've no cause to be."

"I wonder," said Poirot noncommittally.

Sir Guy leaned forward.

"Surely," he cried incredulously, "you cannot believe in—oh, but the thing's absurd! You can know nothing of Ancient Egypt if you think that."

12 **septicemia:** blood poisoning.

A wooden jackal guards the entrance to the tomb's treasury.

For answer Poirot produced a little book from his pocket—an ancient tattered volume. As he held it out I saw its title, *The Magic of the Egyptians and Chaldeans*. Then, wheeling around, he strode out of the tent. The doctor stared at me.

"What is his little idea?"

The phrase, so familiar on Poirot's lips, made me smile as it came from another.

"I don't know exactly," I confessed. "He's got some plan of exorcizing the evil spirits, I believe."

I went in search of Poirot, and found him talking to the lean-faced young man who had been the late Mr. Bleibner's secretary.

"No," Mr. Harper was saying, "I've only been six months with the expedition. Yes, I knew Mr. Bleibner's affairs pretty well."

"Can you recount to me anything concerning his nephew?"

"He turned up here one day, not a bad-looking fellow. I'd never met him before, but some of the others had—Ames, I think, and Schneider. The old man wasn't at all pleased to see him. They were at it in no time, hammer and tongs. 'Not a cent,' the old man shouted. 'Not one cent now or when I'm dead. I intend to leave my money to the furtherance of my life's work. I've been talking it over with Mr. Schneider today.' And a bit more of the same. Young Bleibner lit out for Cairo right away."

"Was he in perfectly good health at the time?"

"The old man?"

"No, the young one."

"I believe he did mention there was something wrong with him. But it couldn't have been anything serious, or I should have remembered."

"One thing more, has Mr. Bleibner left a will?"

"So far as we know, he has not."

"Are you remaining with the expedition, Mr. Harper?"

"No, sir, I am not. I'm for New York as soon as I can square up things here. You may laugh if you like, but I'm not going to be this blasted Men-her-Ra's next victim. He'll get me if I stop here."

A workman helps Carter carry a funeral couch from the tomb.

The young man wiped the perspiration from his brow.

Poirot turned away. Over his shoulder he said with a peculiar smile:

"Remember, he got one of his victims in New York."

"Oh, hell!" said Mr. Harper forcibly.

"That young man is nervous," said Poirot thoughtfully. "He is on the edge, but absolutely on the edge."

I glanced at Poirot curiously, but his enigmatical smile told me nothing. In company with Sir Guy Willard and Dr. Tosswill we were taken around the excavations. The principal finds had been removed to Cairo, but some of the tomb furniture was extremely interesting. The enthusiasm of the young baronet was obvious, but I fancied that I detected a shade of nervousness in his manner as though he could not quite escape from the feeling of menace in the air. As we entered the tent which had been assigned to us, for a wash before joining the evening meal, a tall dark figure in white robes stood aside to let us pass with a graceful gesture and a murmured greeting in Arabic. Poirot stopped.

"You are Hassan, the late Sir John Willard's servant?"

"I served my Lord Sir John, now I serve his son." He took a step nearer to us and lowered his voice. "You are a wise one, they say, learned in dealing with evil spirits. Let the young master depart from here. There is evil in the air around us."

And with an abrupt gesture, not waiting for a reply, he strode away.

"Evil in the air," muttered Poirot. "Yes, I feel it."

Our meal was hardly a cheerful one. The floor was left to Dr. Tosswill, who discoursed at length upon Egyptian antiquities. Just as we were preparing to retire to rest, Sir Guy caught Poirot by the arm and pointed. A shadowy figure was moving amid the tents. It was no human one: I recognized distinctly the dog-headed figure I had seen carved on the walls of the tomb.

My blood froze at the sight.

"Mon Dieu!" murmured Poirot, crossing himself vigorously. "Anubis, the jackal-headed, the god of departing souls."

"Someone is hoaxing us," cried Dr. Tosswill, rising indignantly to his feet.

"It went into your tent, Harper," muttered Sir Guy, his face dreadfully pale.

"No," said Poirot, shaking his head, "into that of Dr. Ames."

The doctor stared at him incredulously; then repeating Dr. Tosswill's words, he cried:

"Someone is hoaxing us. Come, we'll soon catch the fellow."

He dashed energetically in pursuit of the shadowy apparition. I followed him, but, search as we would, we could find no trace of any living soul having passed that way. We returned, somewhat disturbed in mind, to find Poirot taking energetic measures, in his own way, to ensure his personal safety. He was busily surrounding our tent with various diagrams and inscriptions which he was drawing in the sand. I recognized the five-pointed star or Pentagon many times repeated. As was his wont, Poirot was at the same time delivering an impromptu lecture on witchcraft and magic in general, White magic as opposed to Black, with various references to the Ka and the Book of the Dead thrown in.

It appeared to excite the liveliest contempt in Dr. Tosswill, who drew me aside, literally snorting with rage.

"Balderdash, sir," he exclaimed angrily. "Pure balderdash. The man's an impostor. He doesn't know the difference between the superstitions of the Middle Ages and the beliefs of Ancient Egypt. Never have I heard such a hotch-potch of ignorance and credulity."

I calmed the excited expert, and joined Poirot in the tent. My little friend was beaming cheerfully.

"We can now sleep in peace," he declared happily. "And I can do with some sleep. My head, it aches abominably. Ah, for a good tisane!"[13]

As though in answer to prayer, the flap of the tent was lifted and Hassan appeared, bearing a steaming cup, which he offered to Poirot. It proved to be camomile tea, a beverage of which he is inordinately fond. Having thanked Hassan and refused his offer of another cup for myself, we were left alone once more. I stood at the door of the tent some time after undressing, looking out over the desert.

"A wonderful place," I said aloud, "and a wonderful work. I can feel the fascination. This desert life, this probing into the heart of a vanished civilization. Surely, Poirot, you, too, must feel the charm?"

I got no answer, and I turned, a little annoyed. My annoyance was quickly changed to concern. Poirot was lying back across the rude couch, his face horribly convulsed. Beside him was the empty cup. I rushed to his side, then dashed out and across the camp to Dr. Ames's tent.

"Dr. Ames!" I cried. "Come at once."

"What's the matter?" said the doctor, appearing in pajamas.

"My friend. He's ill. Dying. The camomile tea. Don't let Hassan leave the camp."

Like a flash the doctor ran to our tent. Poirot was lying as I left him.

"Extraordinary," cried Ames. "Looks like a seizure—or—what did you say about something he drank?" He picked up the empty cup.

"Only I did not drink it!" said a placid voice.

We turned in amazement. Poirot was sitting up on the bed. He was smiling.

"No," he said gently. "I did not drink it. While my good friend Hastings was apostrophizing the night, I took the opportunity of pouring it, not down my throat, but into a little bottle. That little bottle will go to the analytical chemist. No,"—as the doctor made a sudden movement—"as a

---

13 **tisane:** an herbal tea.

sensible man, you will understand that violence will be of no avail. During Hastings's absence to fetch you, I have had time to put the bottle in safe keeping. Ah, quick, Hastings, hold him!"

I misunderstood Poirot's anxiety. Eager to save my friend, I flung myself in front of him. But the doctor's swift movement had another meaning. His hand went to his mouth, a smell of bitter almonds filled the air, and he swayed forward and fell.

"Another victim," said Poirot gravely, "but the last. Perhaps it is the best way. He has three deaths on his head."

"Dr. Ames?" I cried, stupefied. "But I thought you believed in some occult influence?"

"You misunderstood me, Hastings. What I meant was that I believe in the terrific force of superstition. Once you get firmly established that a series of deaths are supernatural, you might almost stab a man in broad daylight, and it would still be put down to the curse, so strongly is the instinct of the supernatural implanted in the human race. I suspected from the first that a man was taking advantage of that instinct. The

Carter directs the removal of objects from the tomb.

idea came to him, I imagine, with the death of Sir John Willard. A fury of superstition arose at once. As far as I could see, nobody could derive any particular profit from Sir John's death. Mr. Bleibner was a different case. He was a man of great wealth. The information I received from New York contained several suggestive points. To begin with, young Bleibner was reported to have said he had a good friend in Egypt from whom he could borrow. It was tacitly understood that he meant his uncle, but it seemed to me that in that case he would have said so outright. The words suggest some boon companion of his own. Another thing, he scraped up enough money to take him to Egypt, his uncle refused outright to advance him a penny, yet he was able to pay the return passage to New York. Someone must have lent him the money."

"All that was very thin," I objected.

"But there was more. Hastings, there occur often enough words spoken metaphorically which are taken literally. The opposite can happen too. In this case, words which were meant literally were taken metaphorically. Young Bleibner wrote plainly enough: 'I am a leper,' but nobody realized that he shot himself because he believed that he contracted the dread disease of leprosy."

"What?" I ejaculated.

"It was the clever invention of a diabolical mind. Young Bleibner was suffering from some minor skin trouble; he had lived in the South Sea islands, where the disease is common enough. Ames was a former friend of his, and a well-known medical man, he would never dream of doubting his word. When I arrived here, my suspicions were divided between Harper and Dr. Ames, but I soon realized that only the doctor could have perpetrated and concealed the crimes, and I learn from Harper that he was previously acquainted with young Bleibner. Doubtless the latter at some time or another had made a will or had insured his life in favor of the doctor. The latter saw his chance of acquiring wealth. It was easy for him to inoculate Mr. Bleibner with the deadly germs. Then the nephew, overcome with despair at the dread news his friend had conveyed to him, shot himself. Mr. Bleibner, whatever his intentions, had made no will. His fortune would pass to his nephew and from him to the doctor."

"And Mr. Schneider?"

"We cannot be sure. He knew young Bleibner too, remember, and may have suspected something, or, again, the doctor may have thought that a further death motiveless and purposeless would strengthen the coils of superstition. Furthermore, I will tell you an interesting psychological fact, Hastings. A murderer has always a strong desire to repeat his successful crime, the performance of it grows upon him. Hence my fears for young Willard. The figure of Anubis you saw tonight was Hassan dressed up by my orders. I wanted to see if I could frighten the doctor. But it would take more than the supernatural to frighten him. I could see that he was not entirely taken in by my pretenses of belief in the occult. The little comedy I played for him did not deceive him. I suspected that he would endeavor to make me the next victim. Ah, but in spite of *la mer maudite*,[14] the heat abominable, and the annoyances of the sand, the little gray cells still functioned!"

Poirot proved to be perfectly right in his premises. Young Bleibner, some years ago, in a fit of drunken merriment, had made a jocular will, leaving "my cigarette-case you admire so much and everything else of which I die possessed which will be principally debts to my good friend Robert Ames who once saved my life from drowning."

The case was hushed up as far as possible, and, to this day, people talk of the remarkable series of deaths in connection with the Tomb of Men-her-Ra as a triumphal proof of the vengeance of a bygone king upon the desecrators of his tomb—a belief which, as Poirot pointed out to me, is contrary to all Egyptian belief and thought. ∾

14 *la mer maudite:* the awful sea.

Detail of Tutankh-Amen's outermost coffin.

# After Agatha Christie

LINDA PASTAN

in the locked room
what cannot happen
happens again
shaped to the size
of a keyhole
death comes reassuring
choosing someone
no one will miss
now everything becomes
a clue
the moon has left
footprints
all over the rug
the tree outside
the window
hides behind
its false beard
of leaves
who did what
precisely when
slyly the clock stops
the blood smells of ink
the revolver shows
its pearl handle
at the end the facts
click into place
comfortably as knitting
each answer marries
its proper question

even the skull
smiles to itself
as the detective tells
how the moon was pure
all along
the tree was merely
a tree
and only I
have no alibi
at all

THE UNEXPECTED ANSWER
1933 René Magritte

# Suspense

MARY HIGGINS CLARK

According to *Webster's Ninth New Collegiate Dictionary*, the definition of suspense is:

1. the state of being suspended, i.e., held in an undetermined or undecided state awaiting further information

2. a) mental uncertainty or anxiety
   b) pleasant excitement as to a decision or outcome

3. the state or character of being undecided or doubtful

Doesn't that say it all? Uncertainty, anxiety, pleasant excitement, indecision, doubt. Ergo! We've got the makings of a suspense novel.

I'm often asked why as a writer I chose this field. I guess that from the beginning it chose me. As a child I loved to hear and tell scary stories. The idea of a lighted candle didn't go over big with the resident adults, so evenings when we kids got together, I'd suggest that we turn out all the lights except one tiny one. Then we'd have a contest to determine who could spin the creepiest yarn.

Mine was likely to start like this: "There's a man outside! He's watching us. Don't turn around. Don't let him know that we see him. He's looking through the window. He's coming to murder one of us. Oh, Mary Katherine, I'm sorry, he's pointing at you."

I loved that game.

The first two short stories that I sold were suspense stories only because I happened to have ideas for them. Unfortunately for my bank account I didn't write suspense again for another twenty years. Then when I decided I wanted to try a novel, I looked at my bookshelves and realized that my reading of choice had always been in the suspense field. The shelves were stacked with Agatha Christie, Sir Arthur Conan Doyle, Josephine Tey, Ngaio Marsh, Daphne du Maurier, Rex Stout, John D. MacDonald, etc., etc., etc.

In the fable of Hansel and Gretel, the children dropped smooth pebbles and breadcrumbs in order to find their way back out of the forest. The birds ate the breadcrumbs.

The suspense writer must drop both real clues and red herrings. Much of the enjoyment for the reader is determining which is which. I had become a reasonably astute reader and decided to give it a shot and see if I could make it as a writer in this field.

Then of course comes the question: What's the plot? I'd been raised hearing about the Lindbergh baby kidnapping. We had a summer cottage at Silver Beach in the Bronx and every once in a while when we passed St. Raymond's cemetery my father would point to the table outside its flower shop and say, "And there, my dear, is where the ransom note for that poor little baby was left."

And so I grew up with the memory of that tragic case, the kidnapping of the golden child of the golden couple. I decided that a kidnapped child would be the subject of my first attempt at a suspense novel. Exactly at the time there was a celebrated court case in progress in New York. A beautiful young mother was accused of the deliberate, cold-blooded murder of her two children.

Mention that case and everyone had an opinion, a very strong opinion. I thought back to my first writing course in which the professor had said, "Take an event that is compelling, dramatic, memorable. Ask yourself two questions, 'Suppose?' and 'What if?' and write a fictional version with the nucleus of that event as the starting point."

I'd followed that advice with several dozen short stories. Now that I was attempting a novel that would concern kidnapping, I asked myself: "Suppose, what if, an innocent young mother is accused and found guilty of murdering her two young children? Suppose she is released from prison on a technicality, flees to Cape Cod, remarries and begins a new life? And suppose seven years later to the day of the first tragedy, the children of her second marriage disappear?"

I thought it was a good premise and began to envision characters. I like to tell a suspense story in as brief a period as possible. That book took place in fourteen hours. It took three years to write. I still remember the moment when I finally carried the manuscript under my arm and dropped it off at my agent's office. A couple of months passed. Two publishers turned it down because they felt that children in jeopardy might upset their women readers. Then came that marvelous day when I received the call. Simon & Schuster wanted to buy it. I thought I'd died and gone to heaven.

It is a great honor for me that *Where Are the Children?* had now been included in the suspense category, especially in view of the other writers whose company I keep.

No one writer can speak for all writers. We choose our subjects and tell our tales in different ways. But if I were asked how I perceive suspense I would say that suspense is created when the ordinary becomes extraordinary, the familiar becomes chilling.

Ten of us meet for dinner once a month to talk about mystery and suspense. We briefly discuss our current work in progress, exchange ideas, methods of research, setting, plots.

We talk about which comes first, plot or character, or if they are synonymous.

One night we talked about the scariest sound.

The suggestions: a scream, a gunshot, shattering glass. . . . Then came the one that I loved: "The house is completely locked up. You're alone in bed. It's late and dark. And the toilet flushes." The familiar became chilling.

For the rest of it, in my own attempts, I love the idea that the reader is one step ahead of the main character and worried about her. "Don't get in the car with him, he's a killer."

I love short chapters and multiple viewpoints. It harkens back to the old days at St. Francis Xavier, where you were given a one-line speaking part and then exited from the stage. Say your piece and get lost.

I want to offer to the reader the sense of being on a roller coaster. Remember as a child when you bought your ticket and immediately your heart started pounding? You knew you were going to be scared.

I want the woman to be in jeopardy.

I want the reader to become engrossed, put aside necessary tasks, stay up too late to finish the book.

Why? Because as a writer I've tried to offer what suspense was meant to be, anxiety and pleasant excitement. I know the other writers chosen for this category have succeeded splendidly! I'm glad that some people think I may have as well. ❧

# RESPONDING TO CLUSTER ONE

## WHAT MAKES A MYSTERY?
### Thinking Skill   DEFINING

1. Examine the word choice in Pastan's poem "After Agatha Christie" and list the words and phrases that help **define** a mystery.

2. **Analyze** the plot of either "The Framing Game" or "The Adventure of the Egyptian Tomb." (To analyze means to break something into parts and study each part.) Using the plot diagram below, show how the author organizes and orders the events of the story to generate interest and suspense.

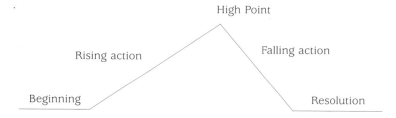

High Point

Rising action

Falling action

Beginning

Resolution

3. In her essay "Suspense," Mary Higgins Clark defines suspense as "anxiety and pleasant excitement." Using this standard, determine which story in this cluster best fits her definition of a mystery. Be prepared to defend your answer.

4. As a class, use the four pieces in this cluster to create a **definition** of mystery.

### Writing Activity: Defining a Mystery
Using the class definition and your own ideas, create your own personal definition of mystery fiction. Your responses to the questions below might be helpful in composing your essay.

• What elements are needed to create a true mystery?

• What is the purpose and appeal of a mystery?

• How are mysteries different from other popular genres—for example, romance, horror, or science fiction?

### A Strong Definition
• begins by stating the term to be defined
• lists the various characteristics or qualities of the term
• organizes information clearly
• ends with a final definition

# CLUSTER TWO

## Whodunit?

Thinking Skill  INVESTIGATING

# This One's on Me

EDWARD HUNSBURGER

**S**am Banner paused in the doorway to knock a thick frosting of powdered snow from his boots. As Green River's Chief of Police, he knew it was important not to "track up" the scene of a crime. It made no difference to Sam that the crime was a minor one which had already been solved or that the cafe's worn, brown linoleum floor obviously held no clues. He liked to do things by the book.

Banner was a big, broad-shouldered man with a sand-colored beard and a head as smooth and hairless as a riverbed rock. He pulled an old Dunhill pipe and a tobacco pouch out of the pocket of his sheepskin coat, and began to load the briar. "Well, Tom," he asked, "what happened here?"

Tom DeBaer grinned. "Just what I told you on the phone, Chief. It's a clear-cut case: assault with intent to rob." He pointed to a thin stranger in a shabby overcoat who was sitting at the counter with his hands cuffed behind his back. "I was just coming in the door, when the suspect practically fell into my arms. He had socked Mr. Panzer on the head, scooped up a handful of coins, and he was fleeing the scene when he ran right into me. It couldn't have been any neater if I planned it myself."

Sam looked at DeBaer with bewilderment. "Mr. Panzer? Coins? You mean to tell me that this man committed assault for a handful of change?"

DeBauer's grin widened. He was really enjoying himself. "Not just ordinary coins, Chief. Rare coins. Mr. Panzer is a rare coin dealer from St. Paul."

Now Sam understood. "Nice work, DeBaer."

"Thanks, Chief. But it was just luck, to be honest."

Sam bit into the stem of his pipe. He wished DeBaer wouldn't call him Chief. It got on his nerves. Everyone else, from the mayor on down, called him Sam. But DeBaer was new to the force, in fact new to Green River itself. He had left the Chicago Police to come to work in Green River, a town of less than 10,000 people. That was two years ago. Since the day of his arrival, DeBaer had made Sam uncomfortable. Time hadn't helped the situation. Sam could fire him, but DeBaer was a good cop and Sam was a fair man. You didn't fire a man just because he made you uncomfortable.

"How about witnesses?" Sam asked.

"Jake was coming out of the kitchen when it happened. He saw the whole thing. Then, of course, there's the victim himself."

The two men looked across the empty cafe to the rear booth where Jake, the owner, was carrying on a low-voiced conversation with a well-dressed, elderly man.

"That's Panzer, Chief. I'll have to take him down to the station so that he can file a complaint. I hope he doesn't mind riding in the same car as the prisoner."

The old man seemed to sense that he was being talked about. He slid out of the booth and hurried over to where Sam and DeBaer were standing.

"Lock the door! Don't let anyone out," he shouted. His whole body was literally dancing with agitation. "The Lafayette Eagle is missing!"

Sam laid a restraining hand on the old man's arm. "Calm down, Mr. Panzer."

"I will not calm down!" He looked at DeBaer. "Officer, I insist that you lock that door immediately."

"Mr. Panzer," Sam began, "I'm Sam Banner, the local chief of police. I don't know how it is in your part of the country, but in Green River you don't order my men around. Now, what seems to be the problem?"

The admonishment had the effect of a cold shower on Panzer. He slumped into the nearest booth and looked at the two men pleadingly.

"I'm sorry, Chief Banner. I guess I got carried away. I thought I had recovered all of the coins involved in the incident. But I was mistaken. My Lafayette Eagle is still missing, and it has to be somewhere in this room."

Sam nodded to DeBaer, who went over and locked the front door. "From your excitement, I take it the coin is a valuable one?"

The old man paled visibly. "Valuable? The Lafayette Eagle is one of the rarest coins I've ever had the pleasure of handling and I've been in the business for over 40 years."

"What makes this particular coin so valuable?" Sam asked.

"The Lafayette Eagle is unique. The coin was minted by Henry Voigt, the chief coiner of the U.S. Mint, in 1794. It's a small gold piece with an eagle on one side and a profile of the Marquis de Lafayette on the other. Only six coins were ever minted."

"Why only six?" Sam asked with growing interest.

"Politics," Panzer grumbled. "What else? When the coin was struck, the French were at the midway point in their ten-year revolution. President Washington had declared a position of neutrality in 1789, but popular sentiment was strong, both for and against the French cause. Voigt minted the Lafayette Eagle to honor a hero of our revolution. What he didn't realize was that Lafayette was no longer a hero in France. He tried to advocate moderation to the mobs and was forced to flee to Flanders for his life. So, in the interest of diplomacy, the coin was never minted for circulation. Of the six gem specimens struck, only two are known to be in existence today, and one of them is in this room."

Sam relit his pipe. He had been so engrossed in the tale that he hadn't noticed it go out. "Mr. Panzer, you say the coin is valuable. Just how valuable?"

Panzer took a deep breath. "I was carrying the Eagle with me because I was on my way to sell it to a client for two hundred thousand dollars."

"Two hundred thousand dollars!"

The voice, like an echo, seemed to come from one of the second row of booths along the opposite wall. Everyone turned toward the area.

A red-faced man sat slowly upright and blinked his eyes. "Morning, all. Did I just hear someone mention a rather large sum of money?"

"What are you doing here?" Sam demanded.

Carl Stranger, reporter for the *Green River Sentinel*, smiled. "I felt a touch of vertigo after eating one of Jake's blue plate specials so I just stretched out for a little nap. What's going on, Sam?"

"Vertigo, my foot," Jake growled. "I thought he had walked out without paying again."

Sam laid a restraining hand on Jake's shoulder. The reporter's presence was going to make the search for the missing coin just that much harder. Sam always thought of Carl Stranger as part of Green River's local color. He drank a little too much, gambled a little too much, and went around getting people's backs up far too much. Basically he wasn't a bad man, he just rubbed people the wrong way. Sam took him aside and briefly explained the situation.

"That's terrific," Stranger said after Sam had finished the story. "It's the first scoop I've had since the mayor's wife brained him with the Christmas tree last year. I'd better phone it right in."

"Hold it, Carl. I'm afraid I can't let you do that just yet. If you phone the paper there's going to be a mob down here within minutes. If, on the other hand, we keep this quiet for a few hours, we can conduct the search without being disturbed. Either way, you still get your scoop. Okay?"

Stranger looked wistfully at the old wooden phone booth in the front of the cafe and then back at Sam. "Okay, provided that I get to help with this glorified egg hunt."

Sam nodded his agreement. He asked Jake to pull down the shades and put the "closed" sign in the front window. Everyone gathered around Green River's Chief of Police, except for the prisoner, who had fallen asleep with his head resting on the lunch counter.

"I think we all have an interest in helping Mr. Panzer recover his missing coin. If any one of you doesn't want to help with the search, he can leave . . . after he's been thoroughly searched by Tom and myself." Sam paused to let the words sink in. After a moment of silence everyone agreed to help look for the missing Eagle.

Sam looked at the elderly coin dealer. "Mr. Panzer, it might make things easier if you told us exactly what happened."

"Well, I was sitting in the back booth with Mr. Lyons," he nodded in Jake's direction, "showing him a few items I thought he might be interested in . . ."

"I didn't know you collected coins, Jake," Sam interrupted.

"Only in a small way, Sam."

Mr. Panzer cleared his throat. "As I was saying . . . I was showing Mr. Lyons some coins. I had about a dozen out of the envelopes and spread out on a small velvet examining board I use, when the thief walked by the table on his way to use the restroom. Foolishly, I had mentioned the Lafayette Eagle to Mr. Lyons. I guess when you make the acquisition of a lifetime it's difficult not to boast about it. He asked to see it, and I saw no reason not to show it to him. I had just placed it on the board when," Mr. Panzer glared at his slumbering aggressor, "that man tried to rob me."

"How exactly did he go about it?" Sam asked.

"He stepped out of the restroom and hit me on the head with his fist. Mr. Lyons jumped up, the man shoved him back in the booth. Then he scooped up the coins from the board and bolted for the front door, where," the old man smiled, "he ran right into Officer DeBaer."

"And then?" Sam prompted.

"Your officer realized the situation immediately and grabbed the man. During the scuffle the thief dropped the coins. By the time Officer DeBaer had the man handcuffed, Mr. Lyons and I were sufficiently recovered to pick up the scattered coins. We brought the coins back to the table while Officer DeBaer phoned you. I didn't realize the Eagle was still missing until you arrived."

Sam looked at Jake who nodded agreement. "One other thing," Sam said. "Has anyone entered or left here since the incident took place?"

"Only you, Chief," DeBaer said, smiling.

"Okay, it's probably someplace up front. Let's divide up that area and start looking."

The search lasted for a little over three hours. It yielded an overdue library book, four pocket combs, a cigarette lighter, and fourteen coins. All of the coins were contemporary and they amounted to a dollar and thirty-five cents. The Lafayette Eagle was still missing.

"Well, we covered every inch of this place twice over," Sam said. "If it's all right with you, Jake, I'd like to try it again tomorrow."

"Can you make it tomorrow morning? I'd like to be able to open by ten if I can."

"Sure, Jake. I'll bring my men over around seven." Sam made an elaborate ritual out of loading and lighting his pipe. What he had to say next he wanted to get right. It wasn't an easy thing to say.

"Except for Mr. Panzer," he began, "I've known most of you a long time. I don't want anyone to take this the wrong way. I think you're all honest men, but the fact of the matter is that the coin is still missing. Before we leave we'll all have to search each other, myself included."

There was a murmur of protest from the group, but finally everyone agreed. "While we're at it," Jake said, "would anyone like a cup of coffee?"

"On the house?" DeBaer asked quickly.

"Yes, on the house, Tom." Jake served coffee to everyone, including the prisoner, who had been awakened for the personal search.

The "on the house" business was another thing about DeBaer that irritated Sam. Sam respected a man who knew the value of money, but Tom

DeBaer was so tight-fisted it made Sam angry. He never socialized with the other men on the force or contributed so much as a quarter to the department's camp program for underprivileged kids. Sam had even known him to go out of his way just to save a dime. Still, it was up to DeBaer to do what he wanted with his own money.

It took almost an hour to search everyone thoroughly. Sam watched as Jake locked the cafe door behind them. That coin, Sam thought, is somewhere inside that room. Why can't we find it?

At ten o'clock that night, Sam was sitting in his oversized easy chair trying to relax. He had a bourbon and water on the sidetable and a book of Conrad's sea stories on his lap. But it just wouldn't work. Every time he started to read he would end up thinking about the missing coin.

There were too many possibilities. Any one of the men could have rehidden the Eagle in an area that had already been searched. Any one of them could have swallowed it with his coffee. Or two of them could have gotten together and passed it back and forth during the personal search.

What about motive? Two hundred thousand dollars was enough to tempt the most honest man. DeBaer liked money too much not to try it. Stranger, with his gambling and drinking, was always in debt. Jake collected coins and he was the one who suggested the coffee. Sam didn't know Mr. Panzer very well, but the coin was insured. So if he could collect the insurance money and later sell the coin on the quiet? Then there was Bradford, the prisoner. He tried to steal it in the first place; why not again? If there was only a clue that pointed in one direction.

The phone rang and Sam answered it. It was Jake checking to make sure that Sam would be there tomorrow morning at seven. Sam assured him that he would and hung up, irritated at having his chain of thought interrupted.

Sam picked up the book again and started to read. Then suddenly, he had the answer. He tossed the book down and headed for the door.

The sound of someone breaking the back door lock came at 3:10. Sam slipped his luminous dial wristwatch off and put it in his pocket. His legs were cramped from over four hours of sitting almost motionless in the back booth of Jake's cafe. He rechecked the position of his gun and flashlight on the table and then sat back to wait for the thief's next move.

A small pen flashlight went on at the other end of the darkened room. After a few minutes Sam heard the sound of metal against metal, then a snapping noise as something gave way, followed by the jingle of coins. He smiled to himself, took up his gun and flashlight, and started across the room.

"Okay, don't make any sudden moves!" As Sam spoke he clicked on the flashlight. The glare blinded Tom DeBaer as he stood in the phone booth with the coin box in his gloved hands.

"What . . . how . . . ," DeBaer sputtered.

"Just put the box down and hand over your gun and badge. You know me well enough not to try anything funny."

DeBaer complied silently. Sam handcuffed him and told him to sit down in one of the booths. He went over and brought the coin box back to the table.

"I don't understand how you figured it out," DeBaer said quietly.

"It was easy." Sam emptied the box out on the table. In the pile of silver a small gold coin glowed. Sam inspected the Lafayette Eagle and then slipped it into his shirt pocket. "You gave yourself away," he said, after a moment's silence.

"But how?"

"You're a tightwad, DeBaer. You never spend a dime on anything you don't have to. But you did today. You called me without leaving this room. You used the pay phone in here when you could have walked out to the curb and called me for free on your car radio."

"I want to talk to a lawyer."

"Sure, you can phone from here if you want to." Sam reached into his pocket and pulled out a dime. He slid it across the table to DeBaer. "Go ahead. This one's on me." ∽

# A Poison That Leaves No Trace

SUE GRAFTON

**T**he woman was waiting outside my office when I arrived that morning. She was short and quite plump, wearing jeans in a size I've never seen on the rack. Her blouse was tunic-length, ostensibly to disguise her considerable rear end. Someone must have told her never to wear horizontal stripes, so the bold red-and-blue bands ran diagonally across her torso with a dizzying effect. Big red canvas tote, matching canvas wedgies. Her face was round, seamless, and smooth, her hair a uniformly dark shade that suggested a rinse. She might have been any age between forty and sixty. "You're not Kinsey Millhone," she said as I approached.

"Actually, I am. Would you like to come in?" I unlocked the door and stepped back so she could pass in front of me. She was giving me the once-over, as if my appearance was as remarkable to her as hers was to me.

She took a seat, keeping her tote squarely on her lap. I went around to my side of the desk, pausing to open the French doors before I sat down. "What can I help you with?"

She stared at me openly. "Well, I don't know. I thought you'd be a man. What kind of name is Kinsey? I never heard such a thing."

"My mother's maiden name. I take it you're in the market for a private investigator."

"I guess you could say that. I'm Shirese Dunaway, but everybody calls me Sis. Exactly how long have you been doing this?" Her tone was a perfect mating of skepticism and distrust.

"Six years in May. I was with the police department for two years before that. If my being a woman bothers you, I can recommend another agency. It won't offend me in the least."

"Well, I might as well talk to you as long as I'm here. I drove all the way up from Orange County. You don't charge for a consultation, I hope."

"Not at all. My regular fee is thirty dollars an hour plus expenses, but only if I believe I can be of help. What sort of problem are you dealing with?"

"Thirty dollars an hour! My stars. I had no idea it would cost so much."

"Lawyers charge a hundred and twenty," I said with a shrug.

"I know, but that's in case of a lawsuit. Contingency, or whatever they call that. Thirty dollars an hour . . ."

I closed my mouth and let her work it out for herself. I didn't want to get into an argument with the woman in the first five minutes of our relationship. I tuned her out, watching her lips move while she decided what to do.

"The problem is my sister," she said at long last. "Here, look at this." She handed me a little clipping from the Santa Teresa newspaper. The death notice read: "Crispin, Margery, beloved mother of Justine, passed away on December 10. Private arrangements. Wynington-Blake Mortuary."

"Nearly two months ago," I remarked.

"Nobody even told me she was sick! That's the point," Sis Dunaway snapped. "I wouldn't know to this day if a former neighbor hadn't spotted this and cut it out." She tended to speak in an indignant tone regardless of the subject.

"You just received this?"

"Well, no. It came back in January, but of course I couldn't drop everything and rush right up. This is the first chance I've had. You can probably appreciate that, upset as I was."

"Absolutely," I said. "When did you last talk to Margery?"

"I don't remember the exact date. It had to be eight or ten years back. You can imagine my shock! To get something like this out of a clear blue sky."

I shook my head. "Terrible," I murmured. "Have you talked to your niece?"

She gestured dismissively. "That Justine's a mess. Marge had her hands full with that one," she said. "I stopped over to her place and you should have seen the look I got. I said, 'Justine, whatever in the world did Margery die of?' And you know what she said? Said, 'Aunt Sis, her heart give out.' Well, I knew that was bull the minute she said it. We have never had heart trouble in our family . . . ."

She went on for a while about what everybody'd died of; Mom, Dad, Uncle Buster, Rita Sue. We're talking cancer, lung disorders, an aneurysm[1] or two. Sure enough, no heart trouble. I was making sympathetic noises, just to keep the tale afloat until she got to the point. I jotted down a few notes, though I never did quite understand how Rita Sue was related. Finally, I said, "Is it your feeling there was something unusual in your sister's death?"

She pursed her lips and lowered her gaze. "Let's put it this way. I can smell a rat. I'd be willing to bet Justine had a hand in it."

"Why would she do that?"

"Well, Marge had that big insurance policy. The one Harley took out in 1966. If that's not a motive for murder, I don't know what is." She sat back in her chair, content that she'd made her case.

"Harley?"

"Her husband . . . until he passed on, of course. They took out policies on each other and after he went, she kept up the premiums on hers. Justine was made the beneficiary.[2] Marge never remarried and with Justine on the policy, I guess she'll get all the money and do I don't know what. It just doesn't seem right. She's been a sneak all her natural life. A regular con artist. She's been in jail four times! My sister talked till she was blue in the face, but she never could get Justine to straighten up her act."

"How much money are we talking about?"

"A hundred thousand dollars," she said. "Furthermore, them two never did get along. Fought like cats and dogs since the day Justine was born. Competitive? My God. Always trying to get the better of each other. Justine as good as told me they had a falling-out not two months before her mother died! The two had not exchanged a word since the day Marge got mad and stomped off."

"They lived together?"

"Well, yes, until this big fight. Next thing you know, Marge is dead. You tell me there's not something funny going on."

"Have you talked to the police?"

"How can I do that? I don't have any proof."

---

1 **aneurysm:** blood-filled blood vessel resulting from disease. If not treated, an aneurysm can burst and cause injury or death.

2 **beneficiary:** the person designated to receive the income from a trust, estate, or insurance policy.

"What about the insurance company? Surely, if there were something irregular about Marge's death, the claims investigator would have picked up on it."

"Oh, honey, you'd think so, but you know how it is. Once a claim's been paid, the insurance company doesn't want to hear. Admit they made a mistake? Uh-uh, no thanks. Too much trouble going back through all the paperwork. Besides, Justine would probably turn around and sue 'em within an inch of their life. They'd rather turn a deaf ear and write the money off."

"When was the claim paid?"

"A week ago, they said."

I stared at her for a moment, considering. "I don't know what to tell you, Ms. Dunaway . . . ."

"Call me Sis. I don't go for that Ms. bull."

"All right, Sis. If you're really convinced Justine's implicated in her mother's death, of course I'll try to help. I just don't want to waste your time."

"I can appreciate that," she said.

I stirred in my seat. "Look, I'll tell you what let's do. Why don't you pay me for two hours of my time. If I don't come up with anything concrete in that period, we can have another conversation and you can decide then if you want me to proceed."

"Sixty dollars," she said.

"That's right. Two hours."

"Well, all right. I guess I can do that." She opened her tote and peeled six tens off a roll of bills she'd secured with a rubber band. I wrote out an abbreviated version of a standard contract. She said she'd be staying in town overnight and gave me the telephone number at the motel where she'd checked in. She handed me the death notice. I made sure I had her sister's full name and the exact date of her death and told her I'd be in touch.

My first stop was the Hall of Records at the Santa Teresa County Courthouse two and a half blocks away. I filled out a copy order, supplying the necessary information, and paid seven bucks in cash. An hour later, I returned to pick up the certified copy of Margery Crispin's death certificate. Cause of death was listed as a "myocardial infarction." The certificate was signed by Dr. Yee, one of the contract pathologists[3] out at

3 **pathologists:** scientists who study diseases; pathologists may also investigate the cause of death.

the county morgue. If Marge Crispin had been the victim of foul play, it was hard to believe Dr. Yee wouldn't have spotted it.

I swung back by the office and picked up my car, driving over to Wynington-Blake, the mortuary listed in the newspaper clipping. I asked for Mr. Sharonson, whom I'd met when I was working on another case. He was wearing a somber charcoal-gray suit, his tone of voice carefully modulated to reflect the solemnity of his work. When I mentioned Marge Crispin, a shadow crossed his face.

"You remember the woman?"

"Oh, yes," he said. He closed his mouth then, but the look he gave me was eloquent.

I wondered if funeral home employees took a loyalty oath, vowing never to divulge a single fact about the dead. I thought I'd prime the pump a bit. Men are worse gossips than women once you get 'em going. "Mrs. Crispin's sister was in my office a little while ago and she seems to think there was something . . . uh, irregular about the woman's death."

I could see Mr. Sharonson formulate his response. "I wouldn't say there was anything irregular about the woman's death, but there was certainly something sordid about the circumstances."

"Oh?" said I.

He lowered his voice, glancing around to make certain we couldn't be overheard. "The two were estranged. Hadn't spoken for months as I understand it. The woman died alone in a seedy hotel on lower State Street. She drank."

"Nooo," I said, conveying disapproval and disbelief.

"Oh, yes," he said. "The police picked up the body, but she wasn't identified for weeks. If it hadn't been for the article in the paper, her daughter might not have ever known."

"What article?"

"Oh, you know the one. There's that columnist for the local paper who does all those articles about the homeless. He did a write-up about the poor woman. 'Alone in Death' I think it was called. He talked about how pathetic this woman was. Apparently, when Ms. Crispin read the article, she began to suspect it might be her mother. That's when she went out there to take a look."

"Must have been a shock," I said. "The woman did die of natural causes?"

"Oh, yes."

"No evidence of trauma, foul play, anything like that?"

"No, no, no. I tended her myself and I know they ran toxicology[4] tests. I guess at first they thought it might be acute alcohol poisoning, but it turned out to be her heart."

I quizzed him on a number of possibilities, but I couldn't come up with anything out of the ordinary. I thanked him for his time, got back in my car, and drove over to the trailer park where Justine Crispin lived.

The trailer itself had seen better days. It was moored in a dirt patch with a wooden crate for an outside step. I knocked on the door, which opened about an inch to show a short strip of round face peering out at me. "Yes?"

"Are you Justine Crispin?"

"Yes."

"I hope I'm not bothering you. My name is Kinsey Millhone. I'm an old friend of your mother's and I just heard she passed away."

The silence was cautious. "Who'd you hear that from?"

I showed her the clipping. "Someone sent me this. I couldn't believe my eyes. I didn't even know she was sick."

Justine's eyes darkened with suspicion. "When did you see her last?"

I did my best to imitate Sis Dunaway's folksy tone. "Oh, gee. Must have been last summer. I moved away in June and it was probably some time around then because I remember giving her my address. It was awfully sudden, wasn't it?"

"Her heart give out."

"Well, the poor thing, and she was such a love." I wondered if I'd laid it on too thick. Justine was staring at me like I'd come to the wrong place. "Would you happen to know if she got my last note?" I asked.

"I wouldn't know anything about that."

"Because I wasn't sure what to do about the money."

"She owed you money?"

"No, no. I owed her . . . which is why I wrote."

Justine hesitated. "How much?"

"Well, it wasn't much," I said, with embarrassment. "Six hundred dollars, but she was such a doll to lend it to me and then I felt so bad when I couldn't pay her back right away. I asked her if I could wait and pay her this month, but then I never heard. Now I don't know what to do."

4 **toxicology:** the science of poisons and their effects.

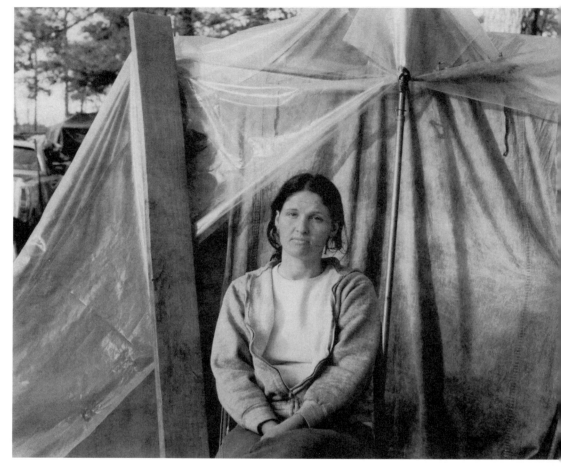

Copyright Joel Sternfeld. Courtesy Pace Wildenstein MacGill, New York

I could sense the shift in her attitude. Greed seems to do that in record time. "You could pay it to me and I could see it went into her estate," she said helpfully.

"Oh, I don't want to put you to any trouble."

"I don't mind," she said. "You want to come in?"

"I shouldn't. You're probably busy and you've already been so nice. . . ."

"I can take a few minutes."

"Well. If you're sure," I said.

Justine held the door open and I stepped into the trailer, where I got my first clear look at her. This girl was probably thirty pounds overweight with listless brown hair pulled into an oily ponytail. Like Sis, she was decked out in a pair of jeans, with an oversize T-shirt hanging almost to her knees. It was clear big butts ran in the family. She shoved some junk aside so I could sit down on the banquette, a fancy word for the ripped plastic seat that extended along one wall in the kitchenette.

"Did she suffer much?" I asked.

"Doctor said not. He said it was quick, as far as he could tell. Her heart probably seized up and she fell down dead before she could draw a breath."

"It must have been just terrible for you."

Her cheeks flushed with guilt. "You know, her and me had a falling out."

"Really? Well, I'm sorry to hear that. Of course, she always said you two had your differences. I hope it wasn't anything serious."

"She drank. I begged her and begged her to give it up, but she wouldn't pay me no mind," Justine said.

"Did she 'go' here at home?"

She shook her head. "In a welfare hotel. Down on her luck. Drink had done her in. If only I'd known . . . if only she'd reached out."

I thought she was going to weep, but she couldn't quite manage it. I clutched her hand. "She was too proud," I said.

"I guess that's what it was. I've been thinking to make some kind of contribution to AA, or something like that. You know, in her name."

"A Marge Crispin Memorial Fund," I suggested.

"Like that, yes. I was thinking this money you're talking about might be a start."

"That's a beautiful thought. I'm going right out to the car for my checkbook so I can write you a check."

It was a relief to get out into the fresh air again. I'd never heard so much horsepuckey in all my life. Still, it hardly constituted proof she was a murderess.

I hopped in my car and headed for a pay phone, spotting one in a gas station half a block away. I pulled change out of the bottom of my handbag and dialed Sis Dunaway's motel room. She was not very happy to hear my report.

"You didn't find anything?" she said. "Are you positive?"

"Well, of course I'm not positive. All I'm saying is that so far, there's no evidence that anything's amiss. If Justine contributed to her mother's death, she was damned clever about it. I gather the autopsy didn't show a thing."

"Maybe it was some kind of poison that leaves no trace."

"Uh, Sis? I hate to tell you this, but there really isn't such a poison that I ever heard of. I know it's a common fantasy, but there's just no such thing."

Her tone turned stubborn. "But it's possible. You have to admit that. There could be such a thing. It might be from South America . . . darkest Africa, someplace like that."

Oh, boy. We were really tripping out on this one. I squinted at the receiver. "How would Justine acquire the stuff?"

"How do I know? I'm not going to set here and solve the whole case for you! You're the one gets paid thirty dollars an hour, not me."

"Do you want me to pursue it?"

"Not if you mean to charge me an arm and a leg!" she said. "Listen here, I'll pay sixty dollars more, but you better come up with something or I want my money back."

She hung up before I could protest. How could she get her money back when she hadn't paid this portion? I stood in the phone booth and thought about things. In spite of myself, I'll admit I was hooked. Sis Dunaway might harbor a lot of foolish ideas, but her conviction was unshakable. Add to that the fact that Justine was lying about something and you have the kind of situation I can't walk away from.

I drove back to the trailer park and eased my car into a shady spot just across the street. Within moments, Justine appeared in a banged-up white Pinto, trailing smoke out of the tail pipe. Following her wasn't hard. I just hung my nose out the window and kept an eye on the haze. She drove over to Milagro Street to the branch office of a savings and loan. I pulled into a parking spot a few doors down and followed her in, keeping well out of sight. She was dealing with the branch manager, who eventually walked her over to a teller and authorized the cashing of a quite large check, judging from the number of bills the teller counted out.

Justine departed moments later, clutching her handbag protectively. I would have been willing to bet she'd been cashing that insurance check. She drove back to the trailer where she made a brief stop, probably to drop the money off.

She got back in her car and drove out of the trailer park. I followed discreetly as she headed into town. She pulled into a public parking lot and I eased in after her, finding an empty slot far enough away to disguise my purposes. So far, she didn't seem to have any idea she was being tailed. I kept my distance as she cut through to State Street and walked up a block to Santa Teresa Travel. I pretended to peruse the posters in the window while I watched her chat with the travel agent sitting at a desk just inside the front door. The two transacted business, the agent handing over what apparently were prearranged tickets. Justine wrote out a check. I busied myself at a newspaper rack, extracting a paper as she came out again. She walked down State Street half a block to a hobby shop where she purchased one of life's ugliest plastic floral wreaths. Busy little lady, this one, I thought.

She emerged from the hobby shop and headed down a side street, moving into the front entrance of a beauty salon. A surreptitious glance through the window showed her, moments later, in a green plastic cape, having a long conversation with the stylist about a cut. I checked my watch. It was almost twelve-thirty. I scooted back to the travel agency and waited until I saw Justine's travel agent leave the premises for lunch. As soon as she was out of sight, I went in, glancing at the nameplate on the edge of her desk.

The blond agent across the aisle caught my eye and smiled.

"What happened to Kathleen?" I asked.

"She went out to lunch. You just missed her. Is there something I can help you with?"

"Gee, I hope so. I picked up some tickets a little while ago and now I can't find the itinerary she tucked in the envelope. Is there any way you could run me a copy real quick? I'm in a hurry and I really can't afford to wait until she gets back."

"Sure, no problem. What's the name?"

"Justine Crispin," I said.

I found the nearest public phone and dialed Sis's motel room again. "Catch this," I said. "At four o'clock, Justine takes off for Los Angeles. From there, she flies to Mexico City."

"Well, that little . . . ."

"It gets worse. It's one-way."

"I knew it! I just knew she was up to no good. Where is she now?"

"Getting her hair done. She went to the bank first and cashed a big check—"

"I bet it was the insurance."

"That'd be my guess."

"She's got all that money on her?"

"Well, no. She stopped by the trailer first and then went and picked up her plane ticket. I think she intends to stop by the cemetery and put a wreath on Marge's grave. . . ."

"I can't stand this. I just can't stand it. She's going to take all that money and make a mockery of Marge's death."

"Hey, Sis, come on. If Justine's listed as the beneficiary, there's nothing you can do."

"That's what you think. I'll make her pay for this, I swear to God I will!" Sis slammed the phone down.

I could feel my heart sink. Uh-oh. I tried to think whether I'd mentioned the name of the beauty salon. I had visions of Sis descending on Justine with a tommy gun. I loitered uneasily outside the shop, watching traffic in both directions. There was no sign of Sis. Maybe she was going to wait until Justine went out to the grave site before she mowed her down.

At two-fifteen, Justine came out of the beauty shop and passed me on the street. She was nearly unrecognizable. Her hair had been cut and permed and it fell in soft curls around her freshly made-up face. The beautician had found ways to bring out her eyes, subtly heightening her coloring with a touch of blusher on her cheeks. She looked like a million bucks—or a hundred thousand, at any rate. She was in a jaunty mood, paying more attention to her own reflection in the passing store windows than she was to me, hovering half a block behind.

She returned to the parking lot and retrieved her Pinto, easing into the flow of traffic as it moved up State. I tucked in a few cars back, all the while scanning for some sign of Sis. I couldn't imagine what she'd try to do, but as mad as she was, I had to guess she had some scheme in the works.

Fifteen minutes later, we were turning into the trailer park, Justine leading while I lollygagged along behind. I had already used up the money Sis had authorized, but by this time I had my own stake in the outcome. For all I knew, I was going to end up protecting Justine from an assassination attempt. She stopped by the trailer just long enough to load her bags in the car and then she drove out to the Santa Teresa Memorial Park, which was out by the airport.

The cemetery was deserted, a sunny field of gravestones among flowering shrubs. When the road forked, I watched Justine wind up the lane to the right while I headed left, keeping an eye on her car, which I could see across a wide patch of grass. She parked and got out, carrying the wreath to an oblong depression in the ground where a temporary marker had been set, awaiting the permanent monument. She rested the wreath against the marker and stood there looking down. She seemed awfully exposed and I couldn't help but wish she'd duck down some to grieve. Sis was probably crouched somewhere with a knife between her teeth, ready to leap out and stab Justine in the neck.

Respects paid, Justine got back into her car and drove to the airport where she checked in for her flight. By now, I was feeling baffled. She had less than an hour before her plane was scheduled to depart and there was still no sign of Sis. If there was going to be a showdown, it was bound to happen soon. I ambled into the gift shop and inserted myself between the wall and a book rack, watching Justine through windows nearly obscured by a display of Santa Teresa T-shirts. She sat on a bench and calmly read a paperback.

What was going on here?

Sis Dunaway had seemed hell-bent on avenging Marge's death, but where was she? Had she gone to the cops? I kept one eye on the clock and one eye on Justine. Whatever Sis was up to, she had better do it quick. Finally, mere minutes before the flight was due to be called, I left the newsstand, crossed the gate area, and took a seat beside Justine. "Hi," I said. "Nice permanent. Looks good."

She glanced at me and then did a classic double take. "What are you doing here?"

"Keeping an eye on you."

"What for?"

"I thought someone should see you off. I suspect your Aunt Sis is en route, so I decided to keep you company until she gets here."

"Aunt Sis?" she said, incredulously.

"I gotta warn you, she's not convinced your mother had a heart attack."

"What are you talking about? Aunt Sis is dead."

I could feel myself smirk. "Yeah, sure. Since when?"

"Five years ago."

"Bull . . . ."

"It's not bull . . . . An aneurysm burst and she dropped in her tracks."

"Come on," I scoffed.

"It's the truth," she said emphatically. By that time, she'd recovered her composure and she went on the offensive. "Where's my money? You said you'd write me a check for six hundred bucks."

"Completely dead?" I asked.

The loudspeaker came on. "May I have your attention, please. United Flight 3440 for Los Angeles is now ready for boarding at Gate Five. Please have your boarding pass available and prepare for security check."

Justine began to gather up her belongings. I'd been wondering how she was going to get all that cash through the security checkpoint, but one look at her lumpy waistline and it was obvious she'd strapped on a money belt. She picked up her carry-on, her shoulder bag, her jacket, and her paperback and clopped, in spike heels, over to the line of waiting passengers.

I followed, befuddled, reviewing the entire sequence of events. It had all happened today. Within hours. It wasn't like I was suffering brain damage or memory loss. And I hadn't seen a ghost. Sis had come to my office and laid out the whole tale about Marge and Justine. She'd told me all about their relationship, Justine's history as a con, the way the two women tried to outdo each other, the insurance, Marge's death. How could a murder have gotten past Dr. Yee? Unless the woman wasn't murdered, I thought suddenly.

Oh.

Once I saw it in that light, it was obvious.

Justine got in line between a young man with a duffel bag and a woman toting a cranky baby. There was some delay up ahead while the ticket agent got set. The line started to move and Justine advanced a step with me right beside her.

"I understand you and your mother had quite a competitive relationship."

"What's it to you," she said. She kept her eyes averted, facing dead ahead, willing the line to move so she could get away from me.

"I understand you were always trying to get the better of each other."

"What's your point?" she said, annoyed.

I shrugged. "I figure you read the article about the unidentified dead woman in the welfare hotel. You went out to the morgue and claimed the body as your mom's. The two of you agreed to split the insurance money, but your mother got worried about a double cross, which is exactly what this is."

"You don't know what you're talking about."

The line moved up again and I stayed right next to her. "She hired me to keep an eye on you, so when I realized you were leaving town, I called her and told her what was going on. She really hit the roof and I thought she'd charge right out, but so far there's been no sign of her. . . ."

Justine showed her ticket to the agent and he motioned her on. She moved through the metal detector without setting it off.

I gave the agent a smile. "Saying good-bye to a friend," I said, and passed through the wooden arch right after she did. She was picking up the pace, anxious to reach the plane.

I was still talking, nearly jogging to keep up with her. "I couldn't figure out why she wasn't trying to stop you and then I realized what she must have done—"

"Get away from me. I don't want to talk to you."

"She took the money, Justine. There's probably nothing in the belt but old papers. She had plenty of time to make the switch while you were getting your hair done."

"Ha, ha," she said sarcastically. "Tell me another one."

I stopped in my tracks. "All right. That's all I'm gonna say. I just didn't want you to reach Mexico City and find yourself flat broke."

"Leave me alone," she hissed. She showed her boarding pass to the woman at the gate and passed on through. I could hear her spike heels tip-tapping out of ear range.

I reversed myself, walked back through the gate area and out to the walled exterior courtyard, where I could see the planes through a wind-break of protective glass. Justine crossed the tarmac to the waiting plane, her shoulders set. I didn't think she'd heard me, but then I saw her hand stray to her waist. She walked a few more steps and then halted, dumping her belongings in a pile at her feet. She pulled her shirt up and checked the money belt. At that distance, I saw her mouth open, but it took a second for the shrieks of outrage to reach me.

Ah, well, I thought. Sometimes a mother's love is like a poison that leaves no trace. You bop along through life, thinking you've got it made, and next thing you know, you're dead. ❧

# Crop Circles

JEROME CLARK AND NANCY PEAR, EDITORS

Crop circles first attracted public attention in the early 1980s, when circular patterns were found in crops of growing grain in the countryside of southern England. Since then they have increased in both number and complexity, and the term now refers to a variety of patterns: from simple single circles to quintuplets (a central circle ringed by four smaller ones), to dumbbell shapes and combinations of these involving lines, bars, ladder-like rungs, and more. These intricate patterns are called "pictograms" because they resemble primitive rock paintings.

"Cereology," the study of crop circles, arose after the *Wiltshire Times* (August 15, 1980) published an article and photographs featuring circles found flattened in a field of oats in Bratton, Wiltshire, England. Each was about 60 feet across and swirled flat in a clockwise direction. The Bratton circles stirred the interest of both meteorologist George Terence Meaden, of the Tornado and Storm Research Organization (TORO), and ufologist Ian Mrzyglod. Mrzyglod made two important discoveries: the circles showed no clear signs of radiation, and they were not really circles at all; the formations were slightly elliptical, an unexpected finding that seemed to argue against a hoax.

A year later, on August 19, 1981, three more circles were found in neighboring Hampshire County, alongside a main highway. Where the Bratton circles appeared random, these at Cheesefoot Head looked as if they had been laid out along a straight line. On either side of the main circle—again 60 feet across—were smaller circles of 25 feet. All were swirled clockwise.

The crop circles seemed to follow a pattern; they appeared mostly during the spring and summer growing season in the rolling grain fields west and southwest of London. This "enchanted" landscape was already home to other archaeological mysteries, including the monoliths of Stonehenge and Avebury, the pyramid-like peak of Silbury Hill, and carvings cut in the chalk hills.

While there is no public database recording the number and types of crop circles that appear yearly, the best available information suggests that during the years 1980 to 1987, between 100 and 120 circles were formed. During that time they also displayed several "mutations." Some circles were swirled counterclockwise; sometimes rings appeared around them. And crop circles varied in size, becoming a great deal larger or smaller.

In 1988 at least 112 circles were recorded, matching the combined total of the eight previous years. In 1989 the number almost tripled, to 305; it tripled again in the summer of 1990 to about 1,000. In 1991 there were 200 to 300 recorded circles, many of them the more complex pictogram type.

By the early 1990s, what had begun with a few simple circles a decade before had mushroomed into a mystery of worldwide scope, with well over 2,000 circles recorded around the globe. Similar circles—though rarely as numerous or complex as those found in England—were now noted in the Soviet Union, the United States, Canada, Australia, Japan, and other countries.

**CHARACTERISTICS** Generally, a crop circle occurs overnight, probably in the hour or two before dawn. It apparently happens in a matter of seconds, usually 60 or less. The line between the affected and non-affected crop is almost always abrupt and dramatic. The flattened area is laid down in a spiral manner from the center outward. In addition, the crop is frequently flattened in layers lying in opposite or differing directions. Once in a while the plant stalks even appear to be braided or intertwined with one another. If a crop circle forms early in the growing season, the affected plants continue to grow and will "bounce back" to nearly normal height. Flattened later in the year, however, the stalks remain on the ground.

The stalks involved are laid down without breaking and show no signs of damage. This is true of even delicate plants, like rape, the source of canola oil. The plant stalks seem to go limp, almost as if they had been steamed or made more elastic. An encircling ring may run counterclockwise to the central circle or vice versa, or both may be laid in the same direction. The smallest crop circle on record measured just eight inches across. And at Alton Barnes in 1990, a pictogram of complex crop circles stretched for nearly an eighth of a mile!

Witnessing the formation of a crop circle is rare. There are roughly three dozen such reports, most collected by Dr. Meaden and his associates at the Circles Effect Research Group (CERES), which is part of TORO. Typical is the account given by Gary and Vivienne Tomlinson published in the *Mail on Sunday* on August 25, 1991, a year after the event took place. The Tomlinsons were walking alongside a field of grain near the village of Hambledon when the plants to their right suddenly started rustling.

"There was a mist hovering above, and we heard a high-pitched sound," said Mrs. Tomlinson. "Then we felt a wind pushing us from the side and above. It was forcing down on our heads so that we could hardly stay upright; yet my husband's hair was standing on end. It was incredible. Then the whirling air seemed to branch into two and zig-zagged off into the distance. We could still see it like a light mist or fog, shimmering as it moved."

Meaden was particularly interested in the Tomlinson account because it seemed to support his own ideas about crop circles. He felt that the simple ones, at least, were formed by the breakdown of a standing, electrically charged whirlwind or plasma-vortex. Unlike regular whirlwinds such as dust devils and waterspouts, which suck in surrounding air, dust, or water at the base of a tunnel of rising air, Meaden's plasma-vortex falls apart, or collapses, in a descending burst of violent wind. It is this collapsing wind-form, surrounded at times by a ring of electrically charged air, that quickly cuts out crop circles. The meteorologist also felt strongly that the low-lying hills of southern England provided the perfect physical conditions for formation of these unusual whirlwinds.

**HOAXES** Some crop circles are believed to be hoaxes. The question remains: how many and which ones? While some cereologists accept pictograms and other complex patterns and formations as genuine, those who believe in a meteorological explanation for the circles feel that anything beyond the simplest shapes are suspicious. Researchers have tried to reach an agreement on guidelines and methods for determining which crop circles are genuine. (Energy "dowsing"— using a divining rod—has been a frequently employed method, for example, but it is highly questionable.)

In most cases, "authentification" still depends on a ground-level, visual inspection of the formation and the experience of the investigator. Sometimes flying over a crop formation is helpful because hoaxes often appear crude or ragged from above.

Probably the biggest crop-circle hoaxers to have come forward are Doug Bower and David Chorley, two elderly Englishmen who claimed to have created some 250 complex formations. On September 9, 1991, the British tabloid *Today* published their detailed confessions. According to the pair, they began their deception in the summer of 1978 with a simple circle near Cheesefoot Head, Wiltshire, that was easily seen from the road. Bower, who had lived in Australia from 1958 to 1966, said he got the idea from the saucer nests that had appeared during that time in Queensland. "We had a good giggle about the first one," Chorley recalled. "It was nice being out on a summer night, so we decided to do some more. But for three rotten years [the papers] never noticed what we were doing."

Bower and Chorley said that once the press and public did take note, they improved their methods and created more complex formations. Frequently they would include their initials—in the form of a double-D— in their handiwork. The two claimed that they finally came forward because others (like Andrews and Delgado, coauthors of two best-selling books on the subject and founders of Circles Phenomenon Research) were profiting from their secret efforts. With *Today*'s help, they created a complex crop formation and invited Delgado to inspect it. Hoaxers Bower and Chorley at last became famous when the investigator declared their formation genuine.

Cereologists were embarrassed by Delgado's mistake. But they challenged Bower and Chorley again. The two made a second daytime circle before the media using the simple tools—string, rope, four-foot-long wooden planks, and a crude sighting device—that they claimed to have used in their early creations. The result was ragged and poorly constructed. (Perhaps more importantly, Bower and Chorley have yet to demonstrate their ability to create a complex crop-circle formation at night, when most appear.) Other groups, including the local Wessex Skeptics, have also created crop circles that have fooled experts.

Yet questions remain about human involvement. Some formations— such as the immense pictogram that appeared at Alton Barnes—are constructed on an enormous scale. Assuming that this and similar formations are hoaxes, why has no huge crop circle ever been discovered interrupted or abandoned—for whatever reason—halfway through completion?

In at least one well-documented case in the summer of 1991, Meaden and a team of visiting Japanese scientists were watching a field with electronic equipment that included radar (sound waves), magnetometers (which measure magnetic force), night-vision video cameras, and motion sensors. Blanketed by mist, a small dumbbell formation appeared; yet none of the sensing equipment noted intruders! In the years since crop circles first appeared, farmers and landowners in the affected areas have watched their property more closely than ever. But the number of hoaxers caught has remained quite small.

**COMPETING THEORIES** UFOs, secret military experiments (that produce microwave or laser radiation), and psychokinesis (the movement of objects with the mind alone) have also been named as causes of crop circles. Doubters, of course, blame human activity—in other words, all crop-circle formations are hoaxes.

Whatever their origins, there is no doubt that English crop circles have captured the imagination of a curious public. For "unlike ghosts, poltergeists, or even UFOs," explained author Hilary Evans, "the circles are absolutely there for anyone to examine at will." ∾

# RESPONDING TO CLUSTER TWO

## WhoDunIt?

## Thinking Skill  INVESTIGATING

1. Investigators often use **motive** (the reason for committing a crime) to lead them to the criminal. What clues lead the Chief to the thief in "This One's on Me"?

2. Trace the steps of **logic** that Kinsey Millhone uses to solve "A Poison That Leaves No Trace."

3. Just because you see or hear a statement in a book, newspaper, or on television does not necessarily make it true. Some people might consider some of the sources in "Crop Circles" questionable. How would you **investigate** whether or not the sources are credible? Use a chart similar to the one below to complete your investigation.

| Source | Credible? | What would you ask to test the source's credibility? |
|---|---|---|
| *Wiltshire Times* | | |
| Dr. Meaden/CERES | | |
| Gary and Vivienne Tomlinson | | |
| Doug Bower and David Chorley | | |
| *Today* (tabloid newspaper) | | |
| Tornado and Storm Research Center | | |

4. **Foreshadowing** is a technique often used by mystery writers to drop hints to the solution. Reread either "A Poison That Leaves No Trace" or "This One's On Me" and list the clues mentioned by the author that might allow you to solve the story.

### Writing Activity: Investigating the Clues

In most mysteries, more than one person is a suspect in the crime. Select one story from this cluster and investigate the suspects in the story. You **investigate** by listing each suspect's alibi, motive for the crime, opportunity, and the facts of the case. Write a summary of your investigation, citing evidence of both the guilt and innocence of your suspects.

### A Strong Summary

- provides an overview of the topic
- highlights important information
- restates the information in your own words

# CLUSTER THREE

## How Do You Solve a Mystery?

Thinking Skill  LOGICAL THINKING

# The Dying Detective

ARTHUR CONAN DOYLE
DRAMATIZED BY MICHAEL AND MOLLIE HARDWICK

## CHARACTERS

Mrs. Hudson

Dr. Watson

Sherlock Holmes

Culverton Smith

## PLACE

Scene One:

*Sherlock Holmes's*
*bedroom, afternoon*

Scene Two:

*The same, dusk*

Scene Three:

*The same,*
*evening*

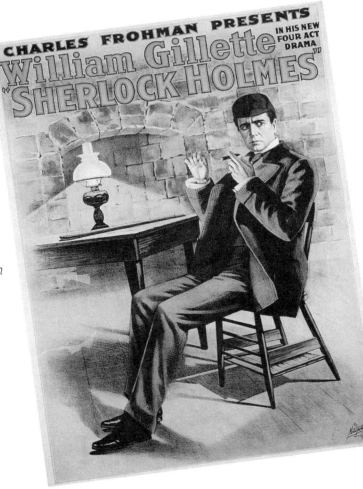

# SCENE ONE

SHERLOCK HOLMES'S *bedroom at 221B Baker Street. The essential features are a bed with a large wooden head, placed crosswise on the stage, the head a foot or two from one side wall; a small table near the bed-head, on the audience's side, on which stand a carafe[1] of water and a glass, and a tiny metal or ivory box; a window in the back wall, the curtains parted; and, under the window, a table or chest of drawers, on which stand a green wine bottle, some wine glasses, a biscuit-barrel, and a lamp. Of course there may be further lamps and any amount of furnishing and clutter:* HOLMES'S *bedroom was adorned with pictures of celebrated criminals and littered with everything from tobacco pipes to revolver cartridges.*

*There is daylight outside the window.* SHERLOCK HOLMES *lies in the bed on his back, tucked up to the chin and evidently asleep. He is very pale.* MRS. HUDSON *enters followed by* DR. WATSON, *who is wearing his coat and hat and carrying his small medical bag.* MRS. HUDSON *pauses for a moment.*

**MRS. HUDSON.** He's asleep, sir.

*(They approach the bed.* WATSON *comes round to the audience's side and looks down at* HOLMES *for a moment. He shakes his head gravely, then he and* MRS. HUDSON *move away beyond the foot of the bed.* WATSON *takes off his hat and coat as they talk, and she takes them from him.)*

**WATSON.** This is dreadful, Mrs. Hudson. He was perfectly hale and hearty when I went away only three days ago.

**MRS. HUDSON.** I know, sir. Oh, Dr. Watson, sir, I'm glad you've come back. If anyone can save Mr. Holmes, I'm sure you can.

**WATSON.** I shall have to know what is the matter with him first. Mrs. Hudson, please tell me, as quickly as you can, how it all came about.

**MRS. HUDSON.** Yes, sir. Mr. Holmes has been working lately on some case down near the river—Rotherhithe, I think.

**WATSON.** Yes, yes. I know.

**MRS. HUDSON.** Well, you know what he is for coming in at all hours. I was just taking my lamp to go to my bed on Wednesday night when I heard a faint knocking at the street door. I . . . I found Mr. Holmes there. He could hardly stand. Just muttered to me to help him up to his bed here, and he's barely spoken since.

---

1 **carafe:** glass bottle for holding drinking water or other liquid.

**WATSON.** Dear me!

**MRS. HUDSON.** Won't take food or drink. Just lies there, sleeping or staring in a wild sort of way.

**WATSON.** But, goodness gracious, Mrs. Hudson, why did you not send for another doctor in my absence?

**MRS. HUDSON.** Oh, I told him straightaway I was going to do that, sir. But he got so agitated—almost shouted that he wouldn't allow any doctor on the premises. You know how masterful he is, Dr. Watson.

**WATSON.** Indeed. But you could have telegraphed for me.

(MRS. HUDSON *appears embarrassed.*)

**MRS. HUDSON.** Well, sir . . .

**WATSON.** But you didn't. Why, Mrs. Hudson?

**MRS. HUDSON.** Sir, I don't like to tell you, but . . . well, Mr. Holmes said he wouldn't even have you to see him.

**WATSON.** What? This is monstrous! I, his oldest friend and . . .

(HOLMES *groans and stirs slightly.*)

Ssh! He's waking. You go along, Mrs. Hudson, and leave this to me. Whether he likes it or not, I shall ensure that everything possible is done.

**MRS. HUDSON.** Thank you, sir. You'll ring if I can be of help.

*(She exits with* WATSON'S *things.* HOLMES *groans again and flings out an arm restlessly.* WATSON *comes to the audience's side of the bed and sits on it.)*

**WATSON.** Holmes? It's I—Watson.

**HOLMES.** *(sighs).* Ahh! Well, Watson? We . . . we seem to have fallen on evil days.

**WATSON.** My dear fellow!

*(He moves to reach for* HOLMES'S *pulse.)*

**HOLMES.** *(urgently).* No, no! Keep back!

**WATSON.** Eh?

**HOLMES.** Mustn't come near.

**WATSON.** Now, look here, Holmes . . . !

**HOLMES.** If you come near . . . order you out of the house.

WATSON. *(defiantly)*. Hah!

HOLMES. For your own sake, Watson. Contracted . . . a coolie disease—from Sumatra.[2] Very little known, except that most deadly. Contagious by touch. So . . . must keep away.

WATSON. Utter rubbish, Holmes! Mrs. Hudson tells me she helped you to your bed. There's nothing the matter with her.

HOLMES. Period of . . . incubation. Only dangerous after two or three days. Deadly by now.

WATSON. Good heavens, do you suppose such a consideration weighs with me? Even if I weren't a doctor, d'you think it would stop me doing my duty to an old friend? Now, let's have a good look at you.

*(He moves forward again.)*

HOLMES. *(harshly)*. I tell you to keep back!

WATSON. See here, Holmes . . .

HOLMES. If you will stay where you are, I will talk to you. If you will not, you can get out.

WATSON. Holmes! *(Recovering)* Holmes, you aren't yourself. You're sick and as helpless as a child. Whether you like it or not, I'm going to examine you and treat you.

HOLMES. *(sneering)*. If I'm to be forced to have a doctor, let him at least be someone I've some confidence in.

WATSON. Oh! You . . . . After all these years, Holmes, you haven't . . . confidence in me?

HOLMES. In your friendship, Watson—yes. But facts are facts. As a medical man you're a mere general practitioner, of limited experience and mediocre qualifications.

WATSON. Well . . . ! Well, really!

HOLMES. It is painful to say such things, but you leave me no choice.

WATSON. *(coldly)*. Thank you. I'll tell you this, Holmes. Such a remark, coming from you, merely serves to tell me what state your nerves are in. Still, if you insist that you have no confidence in me, I will not intrude my services. But what I shall do is to summon Sir Jasper Meek or Penrose Fisher, or any of the other best men in London.

---

2 **Sumatra:** an island in the Indian Ocean.

**HOLMES.** *(groans).* My . . . dear Watson. You mean well. But do you suppose they—any of them—know of the Tapanuli[3] Fever?

**WATSON.** The Tap . . . ?

**HOLMES.** What do you yourself know of the Black Formosa Corruption?

**WATSON.** Tapanuli Fever? Black Formosa Corruption? I've never heard of either of 'em.

**HOLMES.** Nor have your colleagues. There are many problems of disease, many pathological[4] possibilities, peculiar to the East. So I've learned during some of my recent researches. It was in the course of one of them that I contracted this complaint. I assure you, Watson, you can do nothing.

**WATSON.** Can't I? I happen to know, Holmes, that the greatest living authority on tropical disease, Dr. Ainstree, is in London just now.

**HOLMES.** *(beseeching).* Watson!

**WATSON.** All remonstrance[5] is useless. I am going this instant to fetch him. *(He gets up.)*

**HOLMES.** *(a great cry).* No!

**WATSON.** Eh? Holmes . . . my dear fellow . . .

**HOLMES.** Watson, in the name of our old friendship, do as I ask.

**WATSON.** But . . .

**HOLMES.** You have only my own good at heart. Of course, I know that. You . . . you shall have your way. Only . . . give me time to . . . to collect my strength. What is the time now?

*(WATSON sits and consults his watch.)*

**WATSON.** Four o'clock.

**HOLMES.** Then at six you can go.

**WATSON.** This is insanity!

**HOLMES.** Only two hours, Watson. I promise you may go then.

**WATSON.** Hang it, this is urgent, man!

**HOLMES.** I will see no one before six. I will not be examined. I shall resist!

**WATSON.** *(sighing).* Oh, have it your own way, then. But I insist on staying with you in the meantime. You need an eye keeping on you, Holmes.

3 **Tapanuli:** a tiny atoll east of Indonesia in the South Pacific Ocean.

4 **pathological:** concerned with diseases.

5 **remonstrance:** a protest or complaint.

**HOLMES**. Very well, Watson. And now I must sleep. I feel exhausted. *(Drowsily)* I wonder how a battery feels when it pours electricity into a non-conductor?

**WATSON**. Eh?

**HOLMES**. *(yawning)*. At six, Watson, we resume our conversation.

*(He lies back and closes his eyes.* WATSON *makes as though to move, but thinks better of it. He sits still, watching* HOLMES. *A slow black-out.)*


### S C E N E   T W O


*The stage lights up again, though more dimly than before, to disclose the same scene. Twilight is apparent through the window.* HOLMES *lies motionless.*

WATSON *sits as before, though with his head sagging, half-asleep. His chin drops suddenly and he wakes with a jerk. He glances round, sees the twilight outside, and consults his watch. He yawns, flexes his arms, then proceeds to glance idly about him. His attention is caught by the little box on the bedside table. Stealthily, he reaches over and picks it up.*


**HOLMES**. *(very loudly and urgently)*. No! No, Watson, no!

**WATSON**. *(startled)*. Eh? What?

**HOLMES**. Put it down! Down this instant! Do as I say, Watson!

**WATSON**. Oh! All right, then. *(Putting the box down)* Look here, Holmes, I really think . . .

**HOLMES**. I hate to have my things touched. You know perfectly well I do.

**WATSON**. Holmes . . . !

**HOLMES**. You fidget me beyond endurance. You, a doctor—you're enough to drive a patient into an asylum!

**WATSON**. Really!

**HOLMES**. Now, for heaven's sake, sit still, and let me have my rest.

**WATSON.** Holmes, it is almost six o'clock, and I refuse to delay another instant.

*(He gets up determinedly.)*

**HOLMES.** Really? Watson, have you any change in your pocket?

**WATSON.** Yes.

**HOLMES.** Any silver?

**WATSON.** *(fishing out his change).* A good deal.

**HOLMES.** How many half-crowns?

**WATSON.** Er, five.

**HOLMES.** *(sighing).* Ah, too few, too few. However, such as they are, you can put them in your watch-pocket—and all the rest of your money in your left trouser-pocket. It will balance you so much better like that.

**WATSON.** Balance . . . ? Holmes, you're raving! This has gone too far . . . !

**HOLMES.** You will now light that lamp by the window, Watson, but you will be very careful that not for one instant shall it be more than at half flame.

**WATSON.** Oh, very well.

(WATSON *goes to the lamp and strikes a match.*)

**HOLMES.** I implore you to be careful.

**WATSON.** *(as though humoring him).* Yes, Holmes. *(He lights the lamp, carefully keeping the flame low. He moves to draw the curtains.)*

**HOLMES.** No, you need not draw curtains.

(WATSON *leaves them and comes back round the bed.*)

**WATSON.** Well, thank heaven for that.

**HOLMES.** His name is Mr. Culverton Smith, of 13 Lower Burke Street.

**WATSON.** *(staring).* Eh?

**HOLMES.** Well, go on, man. You could hardly wait to fetch someone before.

**WATSON.** Yes, but . . . Culverton Smith? I've never heard the name!

**HOLMES.** Possibly not. It may surprise you to know that the one man who knows everything about this disease is not a medical man. He's a planter.

**WATSON.** A planter!

HOLMES. His plantation is far from medical aid. An outbreak of this disease there caused him to study it intensely. He's a very methodical man, and I asked you not to go before six because I knew you wouldn't find him in his study till then.

WATSON. Holmes, I, . . . I never heard such a . . . !

HOLMES. You will tell him exactly how you have left me. A dying man.

WATSON. No, Holmes!

HOLMES. At any rate, delirious. Yes, dying, delirious. *(Chuckles)* No, I really can't think why the whole ocean bed isn't one solid mass of oysters.

WATSON. Oysters?

HOLMES. They're so prolific,[6] you know.

WATSON. Great Heavens! Now, Holmes, you just lie quiet, and . . .

HOLMES. Strange how the mind controls the brain. Er, what was I saying, Watson?

WATSON. You were . . .

HOLMES. Ah, I remember. Culverton Smith. My life depends on him, Watson. But you will have to plead with him to come. There is no good feeling between us. He has . . . a grudge. I rely on you to soften him. Beg, Watson. Pray. But get him here by any means.

WATSON. Very well. I'll bring him in a cab, if I have to carry him down to it.

HOLMES. You will do nothing of the sort. You will persuade him to come— and then return before him. *(Deliberately)* Make any excuse so as not to come with him. Don't forget that, Watson. You won't fail me. You never did fail me.

WATSON. That's all very well, Holmes, but . . .

HOLMES. *(interrupting)*. Then, shall the world be overrun by oysters? No doubt there are natural enemies which limit their increase. And yet . . . No, horrible, horrible!

WATSON. *(grimly)*. I'm going, Holmes. Say no more, I'm going!

*(He hurries out. HOLMES remains propped up for a moment, staring after WATSON, then sinks back into a sleeping posture as the stage blacks out.)*

---

6 **prolific:** producing many offspring.

# SCENE THREE

*The stage lights up on the same scene.* HOLMES *lies still. It is now quite dark outside. After a moment* WATSON *bustles in, pulling off his coat. He pauses to hand it to* MRS. HUDSON, *who is behind him.*

**WATSON.** Thank you, Mrs. Hudson. A gentleman will be calling very shortly. Kindly show him up here immediately.

**MRS. HUDSON.** Yes, sir. *(She exits.* WATSON *approaches the bed.)*

**HOLMES.** *(drowsily).* Watson?

**WATSON.** Yes, Holmes. How are you feeling?

**HOLMES.** Much the same, I fear. Is Culverton Smith coming?

**WATSON.** Should be here any minute. It took me some minutes to find a cab, and I almost expected him to have got here first.

**HOLMES.** Well done, my dear Watson.

**WATSON.** I must say, Holmes, I'm only doing this to humor you. Frankly, I didn't take to your planter friend at all.

**HOLMES.** Oh? How so?

**WATSON.** Rudeness itself. He almost showed me the door before I could give him your message. It wasn't until I mentioned the name Sherlock Holmes . . .

**HOLMES.** Ah!

**WATSON.** Quite changed him—but I wouldn't say it was for the better.

**HOLMES.** Tell me what he said.

**WATSON.** Said you'd had some business dealings together, and that he respected your character and talents. Described you as an amateur of crime, in the way that he regards himself as an amateur of disease.

**HOLMES.** Quite typical—and surely, quite fair?

**WATSON.** Quite fair—if he hadn't put such sarcasm into saying it. No, Holmes, you said he bears you some grudge. Mark my words, as soon as he has left this house I insist upon calling a recognized specialist.

**HOLMES.** My dear Watson, you are the best of messengers. Thank you again.

**WATSON.** Not at all. Holmes, Holmes—let me help you without any of this nonsense. The whole of Great Britain will condemn me otherwise. Why, my cabmen both enquired anxiously after you; and so did Inspector Morton . . .

**HOLMES.** Morton?

**WATSON.** Of the Yard. He was passing our door just now as I came in. Seemed extremely concerned.

**HOLMES.** Scotland Yard[7] prolific: producing many offspring concerned for me? How very touching! And now, Watson, you may disappear from the scene.

**WATSON.** Disappear! I shall do no such thing. I wish to be present when this Culverton Smith arrives. I wish to hear every word of this so-called medical expert's opinion.

**HOLMES.** *(turning his head).* Yes, of course. Then I think you will just find room behind the head of the bed.

**WATSON.** What? Hide?

**HOLMES.** I have reason to suppose that his opinion will be much more frank and valuable if he imagines he is alone with me.

*(We hear the murmur of* MRS. HUDSON'S *and* CULVERTON SMITH'S *voices offstage.)*

Listen! I hear him coming. Get behind the bed, Watson, and do not budge, whatever happens. Whatever happens, you understand?

**WATSON.** Oh, all right, Holmes. Anything to please you. But I don't like this. Not at all.

*(He goes behind the bed-head and conceals himself.* MRS. HUDSON *enters, looks round the room and then at* HOLMES. SMITH *enters behind her.)*

**MRS. HUDSON.** *(to* SMITH). Oh, Dr. Watson must have let himself out. No doubt he'll be back directly, sir.

**SMITH.** No matter, my good woman. (MRS. HUDSON *bristles at this form of address.)* You may leave me alone with your master.

**MRS. HUDSON.** As you wish—*sir.*

---

7 **Scotland Yard:** the Criminal Investigation Department of London's police headquarters.

*(She sweeps out. SMITH advances slowly to the bed and stands at the foot, staring at the recumbent[8] HOLMES.)*

**SMITH.** *(almost to himself).* So, Holmes. It has come to this, then.

*(HOLMES stirs. SMITH chuckles and leans his arms on the bed-foot and his chin on them, continuing to watch HOLMES.)*

**HOLMES.** *(weakly).* Watson? Who . . . ? Smith? Smith, is that you?

*(SMITH chuckles.)*

**HOLMES.** I . . . I hardly dared hope you would come.

**SMITH.** I should imagine not. And yet, you see, I'm here. Coals of fire, Holmes—coals of fire![9]

**HOLMES.** Noble of you . . .

**SMITH.** Yes, isn't it?

**HOLMES.** I appreciate your special knowledge.

**SMITH.** Then you're the only man in London who does. Do you know what is the matter with you?

**HOLMES.** The same as young Victor—your cousin.

**SMITH.** Ah, then you recognize the symptoms. Well, then, it's a bad look-out for you. Victor was a strong, hearty fellow—but a dead man on the fourth day. As you said at the time, it *was* rather surprising that he should contract an out-of-the-way Asiatic disease in the heart of London—a disease of which *I* have made very special study. *(Chuckles)* And now, you, Holmes. Singular coincidence, eh? Or are you going to start making accusations once again—about cause and effect, and so on.

**HOLMES.** I . . . I knew you caused Victor Savage's death.

*(SMITH comes round the bed.)*

**SMITH.** *(snarling).* Did you? Well, proving it is a different matter, Holmes. But what sort of a game is this, then—spreading lying reports about me one moment, then crawling to me for help the next?

**HOLMES.** *(gasping).* Give . . . give me water. For . . . pity's sake, Smith. Water!

---

8 **recumbent:** lying down, reclining.

9 **coals of fire:** Biblical reference meaning you annoy your enemy when you care for him when he is ill.

(SMITH *hesitates momentarily, then goes to the table and pours a glass from the carafe.*)

**SMITH.** You're precious near your end, my friend, but I don't want you to go till I've had a word with you.

(*He holds out the glass to* HOLMES *who struggles up feebly to take it and drinks.*)

**HOLMES.** (*gulping water*). Ah! Thank . . . thank you. Please . . . do what you can for me. Only cure me, and I promise to forget.

**SMITH.** Forget what?

**HOLMES.** About Victor Savage's death. You as good as admitted just now that you had done it. I swear I will forget it.

**SMITH.** (*laughs*). Forget it, remember it—do as you like. I don't see you in any witness-box, Holmes. Quite another shape of box, I assure you. But you must hear first how it came about.

**HOLMES.** Working amongst Chinese sailors. Down at the docks.

**SMITH.** Proud of your brains, aren't you? Think yourself smart? Well, you've met a smarter one this time.

(HOLMES *falls back, groaning loudly.*)

Getting painful, is it?

(HOLMES *cries out, writhing in agony.*)

**SMITH.** That's the way. Takes you as a cramp, I fancy?

**HOLMES.** Cramp! Cramp!

**SMITH.** Well, you can still hear me. Now, can't you just remember any unusual incident—just about the time your symptoms began?

**HOLMES.** I . . . can't think. My mind is gone! Help me, Smith!

**SMITH.** Did nothing come to you through the post, for instance?

**HOLMES.** Post? Post?

**SMITH.** Yes. A little box, perhaps?

(HOLMES *emits a shuddering groan.*)

**SMITH.** (*closer, deadly*). Listen! You *shall* hear me! Don't you remember a box—a little ivory box? (*He sees it on the table and holds it up.*) Yes, here it is on your bedside table. It came on Wednesday. You opened it—do you remember?

HOLMES. Box? Opened? Yes, yes! There was . . . sharp spring inside. Pricked my finger. Some sort of joke . . .

SMITH. It was no joke, Holmes. You fool! Who asked you to cross my path? If you'd only left me alone I would never have hurt you.

HOLMES. Box! Yes! Pricked finger. Poison!

SMITH. *(triumphantly)*. So you do remember. Good, good! I'm glad indeed. Well, the box leaves this room in my pocket, and there's your last shred of evidence gone. *(He pockets it.)* But you have the truth now, Holmes. You can die knowing that I killed you. You knew too much about what happened to Victor Savage, so you must share his fate. Yes, Holmes, you are very near your end now. I think I shall sit here and watch you die.

*(He sits on the bed.)*

HOLMES. *(almost a whisper)*. The shadows . . . falling. Getting . . . so dark. I can't see, Smith! Smith, are you there? The light . . . for charity's sake, turn up the light!

(SMITH *laughs, gets up, and goes to the light.*)

SMITH. Entering the valley of the shadow, eh, Holmes? Yes, I'll turn up the light for you. I can watch your face more plainly, then.

*(He turns the flame up full.)*

There! Now, is there any *further* service I can render you?

HOLMES. *(in a clear strong voice)*. A match and my pipe, if you please.

*(He sits bolt upright,* SMITH *spins round to see him.*)

SMITH. Eh? What the devil's the meaning of this?

HOLMES. *(cheerfully)*. The best way of successfully acting a part is to *be* it. I give you my word that for three days I have neither tasted food nor drink until you were good enough to pour me out that glass of water. But it's the tobacco I find most irksome.

*(We hear the thud of footsteps running upstairs offstage.)*

Hello, hello! Do I hear the step of a friend.

(INSPECTOR MORTON *hurries in.*)

MORTON. Mr. Holmes?

HOLMES. Inspector Morton, this is your man.

SMITH. What is the meaning of . . . ?

**MORTON.** Culverton Smith, I arrest you on the charge of the murder of one Victor Savage, and I must warn you that anything you say . . .

**SMITH.** You've got nothing on me! It's all a trick! A pack of lies!

*(He makes to escape.* MORTON *restrains him.)*

**MORTON.** Keep still or you'll get yourself hurt!

**SMITH.** Get off me!

**MORTON.** Hold your hands out!

*(They struggle.* MORTON *gets out handcuffs and claps them on* SMITH'S *wrists.)*

That'll do.

**HOLMES.** By the way, Inspector, you might add the attempted murder of one Sherlock Holmes to that charge. Oh, and you'll find a small box in the pocket of your prisoner's coat. Pray, leave it on the table, here. Handle it gingerly, though. It may play its part at his trial.

*(MORTON retrieves the box and places it on the table.)*

**SMITH.** Trial! You'll be the one in the dock,[10] Holmes. Inspector, he asked me to come here. He was ill, and I was sorry for him, so I came. Now he'll pretend I've said anything he cares to invent that will corroborate[11] his insane suspicions. Well, you can lie as you like, Holmes. My word's as good as yours.

**HOLMES.** Good heavens! I'd completely forgotten him!

**MORTON.** Forgotten who, sir?

**HOLMES.** Watson, my dear fellow! Do come out!

*(WATSON emerges with cramped groans.)*

I owe you a thousand apologies. To think that I should have overlooked you!

**WATSON.** It's all right, Holmes. Would have come out before, only you said, whatever happened, I wasn't to budge.

**SMITH.** What's all this about?

**HOLMES.** I needn't introduce you to my witness, my friend Dr. Watson. I understand you met somewhere earlier in the evening.

**SMITH.** You . . . you mean you had all this planned?

10 **dock:** the place where a suspect stands or sits in a court of law.

11 **corroborate:** support, confirm.

**HOLMES.** Of course. To the last detail. I think I may say it worked very well—with your assistance, of course.

**SMITH.** Mine?

**HOLMES.** You saved an invalid trouble by giving my signal to Inspector Morton, waiting outside. You turned up the lamp.

(SMITH *and* WATSON *are equally flabbergasted.)*

**MORTON.** I'd better take him along now, sir. *(To* SMITH) Come on.

*(He bundles* SMITH *roughly towards the door.)*

We'll see you down at the Yard tomorrow, perhaps, Mr. Holmes?

**HOLMES.** Very well, Inspector. And many thanks.

**WATSON.** Goodbye, Inspector.

(MORTON *exits with* SMITH.)

**WATSON.** *(chuckles).* Well, Holmes?

**HOLMES.** Well, Watson, there's a bottle of claret over there—it is uncorked—and some biscuits in the barrel. If you'll be so kind, I'm badly in need of both.

**WATSON.** Certainly. You know, Holmes, all this seems a pretty, well, elaborate way to go about catching that fellow. I mean, taking in Mrs. Hudson—and *me*—like that. Scared us half to death.

**HOLMES.** It was very essential that I should make Mrs. Hudson believe in my condition. She was to convey it to you, and you to him.

**WATSON.** Well . . .

**HOLMES.** Pray do not be offended, my good Watson. You must admit that among your *many* talents, dissimulation[12] scarcely finds a place. If you'd shared my secret, you would never have been able to impress Smith with the urgent necessity of coming to me. It was the vital point of the whole scheme. I knew his vindictive nature, and I was certain he would come to gloat over his handiwork.

(WATSON *returns with the bottle, glasses, and barrel.)*

**WATSON.** But . . . but your appearance, Holmes. Your face! You really do look ghastly.

**HOLMES.** Three days of absolute fast does not improve one's beauty, Watson. However, as you know, my habits are irregular, and such a

---

12 **dissimulation:** hiding the truth; pretending.

feat means less to me than to most men. For the rest, there is nothing that a sponge won't cure. Vaseline to produce the glistening forehead; belladonna[13] for the watering of the eyes; rouge over the cheekbones and crust of beeswax round one's lips . . .

**WATSON.** *(chuckling).* And that babbling oysters!

*(He begins pouring the wine.)*

**HOLMES.** Yes. I've sometimes thought of writing a monograph on the subject of malingering.

**WATSON.** But why wouldn't you let me near you? There was no risk of infection.

**HOLMES.** Whatever I may have said to the contrary in the grip of delirium, do you imagine that I have no respect for your medical talents? Could I imagine that you would be deceived by a dying man with no rise of pulse or temperature? At four yards' distance I *could* deceive you.

(WATSON *reaches for the box.)*

**WATSON.** This box, then . . .

**HOLMES.** No, Watson! I wouldn't touch it. You can just see, if you look at it sideways, where the sharp spring emerges as you open it. I dare say it was by some such device that poor young Savage was done to death. He stood between that monster and an inheritance, you know.

**WATSON.** Then it's true, Holmes! You . . . you might have been killed, too!

**HOLMES.** As you know, my correspondence is a varied one. I am somewhat on my guard against any packages which reach me. But I saw that by pretending he had succeeded in his design I might be enabled to surprise a confession from him. That pretense I think I may claim to have carried out with the thoroughness of a true artist.

**WATSON.** *(warmly).* You certainly did, Holmes. Er, a biscuit?

*(He holds out the barrel.)*

**HOLMES.** On second thoughts, Watson, no thank you. Let us preserve our appetite. By the time I have shaved and dressed, I fancy it will just be time for something nutritious at our little place in the Strand.

*(They raise their glasses to one another and drink. The curtain falls.)* ∾

---

13 **belladonna:** a drug made from a poisonous plant.

# Arsenic and "Old Rough and Ready"

WILLIAM MAPLES

*Duncan is in his grave;*
*After life's fitful fever he sleeps well;*
*Treason has done his worst: nor steel, nor poison,*
*Malice domestic, foreign levy, nothing,*
*Can touch him further. . . .*
—Shakespeare, *Macbeth*, Act III, Scene 2

**S**ummers in Washington, D.C., can be horribly hot, and July 4, 1850, was infernal. President Zachary Taylor, hero of the Battle of Buena Vista in the Mexican War, had just returned from a ceremony in the blazing sun, at which he laid the foundation-stone for the Washington Monument. He was tired, hungry and thirsty. He wolfed down a big meal of raw vegetables, fresh cherries and iced buttermilk. Within a very short time it became apparent that the food had not agreed with him. The President developed gastroenteritis[1] and acute diarrhea and was forced to take to his bed. Five days later, on July 9, the man known to his contemporaries as "Old Rough and Ready" was dead. He was sixty-six years old and had been President just sixteen months.

Taylor's abrupt death came at a crucial point in American history. It removed from the scene a man whose force of character might have

---

1 **gastroenteritis:** inflammation of the stomach and intestines.

Zachary Taylor, 12th president
of the United States.

quelled the storm brewing across America over slavery—or hastened that storm's breaking. Taylor might have recalled his fellow Southerners to a sense of the duty they owed to their country; but it is equally possible that he might have driven them to desperate deeds by opposing them with naked force. We can never know. A single ill-digested meal toppled Taylor into his grave; the rest is guesswork and silence.

Some historians have called Zachary Taylor the Dwight Eisenhower of his day, because of his brilliant military record; but there was an element of fire, of hot-tempered truculence,[2] in Taylor that was wholly missing from Ike's serene, controlled disposition. A Southerner who owned sugar and cotton plantations worked by over four hundred slaves—his daughter, Knox, was the first wife of the man who would become president of the Confederacy, Jefferson Davis, and his son, Richard, served as a general for the South in the Civil War—Taylor nevertheless campaigned hard to admit California and New Mexico as free states and threatened to lead an army in person against any Southerners who would not submit to laws enacted by Congress. When two Southern legislators, Alexander Stephens and Robert Toombs, told Taylor he was betraying the South, the President exploded, saying he would hang all "traitors" to the Union with no more compunction[3] than he had shown when hanging spies and deserters in Mexico. In the days immediately preceding his fatal illness, Taylor ordered the military garrison of Santa Fe, New Mexico, to be reinforced against possible attacks by proslavery militiamen from Texas. He was a tough man, singularly unafraid of his enemies, willing to do battle to keep the United States one nation, indivisible.

His death marked an important crossroads in the crisis over slavery. His successor, Millard Fillmore, was at pains to mollify the angry Southerners whom Taylor had defied. The new President quietly shelved New Mexico's application for statehood and lent his support to a jellified compromise bill that contained all sorts of sops to satisfy both sides of the slavery question. The outbreak of the Civil War was postponed for another decade, and in the awful glare of that cataclysmic passage of arms, the story of Zachary Taylor, his short presidency and his sudden death, receded into oblivion. Few schoolchildren today could name the twelfth President of the United States. The bumbling Millard Fillmore is better known than the hard-bitten hero of Buena Vista.

2 **truculence:** feeling.
3 **compunction:** anxiety which comes from a guilty conscience.

Yet from time to time Taylor's sudden death would tax the ingenuity of amateur historians. Aged sixty-six, he was old but not decrepit. His constitution had been tried and tempered in arduous campaigns in Mexico, and earlier in Florida against the Seminole Indians. He was no stranger to heat and thirst. Could raw vegetables and fruit, washed down with cold milk, kill a man? Books published in 1928 and again in 1940 raised the possibility that Taylor had been poisoned by proslavery conspirators. If so, he, not Abraham Lincoln, would have been the first President in American history to be assassinated.

My mind was far from these theories in 1991, when I received a visit from Clare Rising in the office I then occupied in the Florida Museum of Natural History. Rising was one of our alumnae; she had received her Ph.D. in English from the University of Florida and was the prize-winning author of *Season of the Wild Rose*, a historical novel set during the Civil War. It was while researching this novel that she had come across the Taylor case, and it had fascinated her ever since. She was writing a book about Taylor. She described his symptoms—vomiting, abdominal spasms, diarrhea and progressive weakening—which she had gleaned from contemporary accounts of his death. Was it possible, she asked me, that such symptoms might result from poisoning?

I told Rising that I wasn't a pathologist but that the symptoms she had described certainly could have resulted from arsenic poisoning.

She said: "Well, could this be proven?" And I explained that arsenic and other metallic poisons are quickly deposited in the skeletal system and hair of poisoning victims, if they live for a few days after the initial intake of the poison. Such metals would remain in the hair and bones, even after death.

She asked: "How could this be proven?" I told her it would be a fairly simple matter, given access to the remains, to have tests done that would prove the presence or absence of arsenic.

I gradually discovered that Rising was an extremely persistent and single-minded individual. Initially I had scant interest in the Taylor question, and I tried to steer her toward other people in the field who I felt were perfectly competent to conduct such tests. I suggested she contact my colleague, Doug Ubelaker, at the Smithsonian Institution. I suggested the Armed Forces Institute of Pathology at Walter Reed Hospital. I suggested the Armed Forces Medical Museum. I furnished her with names and telephone numbers.

In vain, Rising kept returning to me. She had a scholarly obsession with Zachary Taylor—"my Zachary," she called him fondly—and she saw this inquiry as a way to do justice to a rather neglected figure in American history. I was less sanguine than she. Moreover the enormity of exhuming[4] a former President of the United States was somewhat daunting. I had assisted at many exhumations, but never at one of such extraordinary historical significance. I had no misgivings about the technical side of the affair. No corpse on earth has the power to overawe me. Our defunct bodies are all equal before science. Nevertheless, I could dimly foresee how controversial this project might prove, and what a fanfaronade[5] of media attention might accompany it. As events were to show, my fears proved justified many times over!

Finally, on the latest of her many visits, Rising sat down in a chair across from my desk and said: "Well, just how would we get permission?"

I explained to her something that many people do not know: human remains are not the property of cemeteries. They don't belong to the nation, no matter who they were in life. Nor do they belong to the courts. They belong to the relatives who survive them. From a legal standpoint, dead human bodies are treated exactly the same as any other personal effect left behind by the deceased. They are passed on, together with the rest of the estate. You own the remains of your dead ancestors. They are yours by law.

Therefore, I told Rising, if anyone wanted to examine a body, the first step must be to approach the surviving family members. These in turn can request a funeral director licensed in the state to open the grave, provided the body is properly reburied upon completion of the examination. I told her that very often in murder cases we go through this procedure, with the families' permission. If the family agrees, we need not go through the courts. This timesaving procedure is especially useful when we are dealing with murder victims who are buried in states other than those where the murders took place.

Rising was elated. She told me she had tracked down many of the living relatives and knew from genealogies who the nearest direct descendant was—and she mentioned a man in Louisiana whose name is familiar to millions of people.

---

4 **exhuming:** removing a body from a tomb, often for scientific study.
5 **fanfaronade:** empty boasting.

I said: "Well, all you have to do is get that gentleman to sign a request that the nearest licensed funeral director open the tomb."

I have already said Rising was persistent. But even I was surprised when she triumphantly telephoned me from Louisiana a few weeks later and announced that she had won permission to exhume the remains of Zachary Taylor. Not only that: she had already approached a funeral director in Louisville, Kentucky, whose firm had moved President Taylor and his wife from an older mausoleum to a newer aboveground tomb in the 1920s. Rising's enthusiasm was contagious. The funeral director said that he would not only cooperate but would perform the exhumation without charge.

Zachary Taylor, I learned, was entombed in the Zachary Taylor National Cemetery in Louisville, Kentucky, which, like all national cemeteries, is supervised by the Veterans Administration. The land for that cemetery had been donated to the federal government by the Taylor family, but they had retained ownership of a strip of land at the rear of the cemetery, on both sides of the Taylor mausoleum, as a private family burial plot. Everything else was under VA stewardship.

I did some soul-searching before agreeing to be present at the exhumation. It is my firm belief that the dead have a right to privacy and that there must be a good, compelling reason for us to break in upon the slumber of the grave. In the case of President Taylor, there was the charge—albeit unproven—of murder, the foulest crime man can commit. For over a hundred and forty years it had hovered around Taylor's memory like a miasma.[6] Now we were in a position to decide once and for all whether or not there was anything to it. The relatives had given their consent. Their scruples had been satisfied that this was a legitimate inquiry, and not an exercise in idle speculation. The local coroner, Dr. Richard Greathouse, had agreed to treat the procedure as an official investigation into the cause of Taylor's death, and he had enlisted the aid of the state medical examiner, Dr. George Nichols IV.

It was the consent of the relatives, however, that weighed most with me. If they saw no indignity in exhuming Taylor, then there was none. Rising had written to family members as far away as Rome and Stockholm, and all had consented to the investigation. The *New York Times* editorialized that our inquiry showed "a cavalier contempt for the

---

6 **miasma:** heavy, vaporous atmosphere.

dead," but I could not agree. It would be frivolous indeed to exhume a President to see if he had suffered from a certain disease, or to learn some small particular about his life and times. But murder is another thing entirely, and murder was what we aimed to prove or disprove.

The team I had put together consisted of myself, Dr. Nichols, Dr. William Hamilton, the District 8 medical examiner in Florida, who had worked for Dr. Nichols before coming to Gainesville (and who had experience in examining the exhumed victims of arsenic poisoning), two graduate students, Arlene Albert and Dana Austin-Smith, who would do the still photography, and a local retired attorney and historian, Bill Goza, who would lend us historical assistance and expedite details. Finally, my wife Margaret, a media specialist who is always an important member of my team, would handle logistics and take care of videotaping the investigation for scientific purposes.

A date was set. We made hotel reservations and rented a van for the following weekend. Then difficulties began to crop up. Rising telephoned me, saying that a problem had arisen with the Veterans Administration. The VA was reluctant to give permission for the exhumation. When I finally reached a high-level official in the VA, he said the matter might have to be resolved at "a higher level."

I said: "What do you mean by 'higher'?"

And he said: "Since it involves the remains of a President, the White House."

By now it was Thursday. The tomb was supposed to be opened the next Monday. There was no way we could secure presidential permission in that short interval. Even though the Taylor family owned the mausoleum and the strip of land adjacent to it, the VA ran the cemetery and had the key to the Taylor crypt. The Zachary Taylor mausoleum was situated at the back of the cemetery, and the VA controlled all the land in front of it. They could simply lock the front gate and there would be little we could do to oppose them.

With some disappointment—for by now I had become rather interested in this project—I phoned Rising and said there was no way we could proceed the following Monday. Perhaps some other time . . . In the meantime all our arrangements were canceled.

Shortly afterward, Rising called me back and said she'd been in contact with the coroner, Dr. Richard Greathouse. He, I discovered, wasn't about to be dictated to by the Veterans Administration. He was a man of extraordinary determination, confidence and a strong sense of territory.

Greathouse told Rising to tell me that whether I came to Louisville or stayed home was all the same to him. I was welcome to be on hand if I liked. But with or without me, Zachary Taylor's tomb was going to be opened that Monday morning and the only way the federal government could prevent this was by armed force!

So, after reassembling all our broken travel arrangements, we left for Louisville on Saturday morning. We arrived Sunday afternoon at the hotel, a Ramada Inn located right beside the Zachary Taylor National Cemetery. As we pulled into the parking lot we were horrified to see a host of satellite dishes, mounted on large vehicles, surrounding the hotel. When I checked into the hotel I learned to my chagrin that I had telephone messages waiting for me from the "Today" show, "Good Morning America," CNN and various other news organizations. Rising met us at the hotel and told us the VA desired a meeting with us right away.

The VA was worried about publicity and I didn't blame them: the whole Taylor exhumation was fast becoming a media circus. The VA was no longer opposed to exhuming Taylor, but it was adamantly opposed to taking pictures of the remains. "No photos," the two representatives told us firmly.

I explained that as forensic scientists we were obligated to document what we did and that we couldn't proceed without photographs.

The VA official said: "How do we know these photographs won't show up in the National Enquirer?"

"Easy," I answered him. "Show me one photograph I've ever taken that has appeared in any newspaper or magazine or publication such as the National Enquirer." I explained that the photos would be used in scientific books, publications and scientific articles. This appeared to satisfy him.

That Sunday evening was one of the most interesting and atmospheric of my life. We went to a reception and dinner at Zachary Taylor's old home, which is located not far behind the cemetery. It is a splendid old dwelling and its owners are devoted to the President's memory. They have delved into every aspect of his life with extraordinary zeal. Other members of the Taylor family were there, including the President's two great-great-great-great granddaughters, a beautiful and vivacious pair of young women who charmed everyone with their lively, sparkling manner. I was amazed to hear that, had the VA forbidden us access, the Taylor family had made arrangements with neighbors whose property abutted the rear of the cemetery, to climb over the wall and enter the mausoleum directly from behind! I was silently relieved matters had not gone so far.

Dinner was served in a gorgeous dining room overhung by magnificent chandeliers. Portraits of Zachary Taylor hung everywhere, and the elegant meal was concluded by a dessert of pecan pie that was said to be an old family recipe, a favorite of the President's. Margaret's health was toasted—it was her birthday—and we both learned wonderful bits of Taylor family lore and heard many fascinating anecdotes about "Old Rough and Ready" from the lips of those to whom he was no remote textbook figure, but a beloved and well-remembered ancestor. Seldom has history come so agreeably to life as it did for me that evening.

Yet at the back of everyone's mind was the dark and fascinating prospect of the next day. We were about to resurrect a dead man, yet the mood was lively, convivial, even festive. There was an indefinable air of keen anticipation: tomorrow morning the President whose likeness hung upon the walls of this dining room, Zachary Taylor himself, would reenter the world of the living. He would step back onto the stage of American history he had suddenly vacated a hundred and forty-one years earlier.

The next morning, whatever hopes we had that the investigation in the cemetery would be conducted quietly and decorously were dashed. When we arrived at the entrance to the cemetery at 9 A.M. we found the fire department at the front gate, directing traffic. Police were everywhere. The main avenue of the cemetery was lined with hundreds of people. Media camera units were positioned in cherry-picker cranes overhead. We were let through a police barrier and parked on the curved drive just in front of the Taylor tomb. Watched by thousands of inquisitive eyes, we unloaded our equipment and proceeded to document the area.

The local funeral director had secured services of some volunteers from a memorial vault company to assist in the delicate task of moving the massive slab of Tennessee marble that sealed the vault containing the coffins of President and Mrs. Taylor. This enormous vault was inside the tomb, with only a couple of feet of clearance on three sides.

When the slab was lifted, a badly rotted wooden casket was seen to be lying within the vault. Inside this casket was a lead liner, all the seams of which had been soldered shut. Under closer examination, we saw a rectangular soldered plate near the head of the liner. Beneath this plate was a cracked glass window. The apparent purpose of this glass window was to allow the dead President to be viewed while lying in state in his coffin at the White House.

We had not expected to find this sealed box of lead and had no tools with which to open it. In any case the mausoleum was so small that there was no room to work or maneuver, and the milling crowds outside were oppressive. We decided to take the lead liner and the enclosed remains to the office of the state medical examiner and to open it there.

Now we were alone at last, and now the true investigation could begin. At the office of the medical examiner, we changed to scrub suits and discussed how the lead liner could best be opened. It looked solid, but we now saw it was pocked with several perforations. Historical records said Taylor had not been embalmed—his wife had forbidden it. Instead, his body had been packed in ice for the lying in state. As his body decomposed within the lead box, the resultant butyric acids[7] had eaten through the metal in several places. So these holes were an important piece of evidence. Because they showed Taylor had not been embalmed, and because arsenic was part of the nineteenth-century embalming process, we could be sure the remains had not been contaminated by an undertaker.

But how to open the box? Initially it was decided to use a small blowtorch. A worker from the maintenance department of the county coroner's office was summoned to the room and, using a small torch attached to a miniature propane tank, he began carefully to melt the solder joints of the casket. Suddenly I had a horrifying thought. Peering through the opened portion of the seam, I could see that the box was lined with cloth! If this cloth liner should catch fire from the flame of the blowtorch, our proposed examination of Zachary Taylor might end with his unexpected cremation! The blowtorch was extinguished instantly and sent back to the basement.

We considered awhile and then fell back on a trusty Stryker saw,[8] the oscillating bladed tool that is used to cut bone in autopsies. This saw went through the lead liner like cheese, and the top popped off as neatly as if we had used a can opener.

The lid was moved out of the way and all of us peered down into the depths of the container. There lay all that remained of President Zachary Taylor.

7 **butyric acids:** acids normally found in perspiration and rancid butter.
8 **Stryker saw:** a specialized saw used to cut through bone.

The former President had been totally skeletonized. Abundant hair could be seen adhering to the skull. The deceased President's bushy eyebrows were still visible, clinging to the supra orbital ridges above his skull's eye sockets. The hair was dark, flecked with gray. For the rest, he presented an austere picture of simple mortality: a skeleton, clad in his funeral attire, his skull pillowed on a bunch of straw stuffed beneath the casket liner. He had one missing tooth and one collapsed crown, but otherwise his teeth were still magnificent. Taylor must have had a brilliant, winning smile in life.

The deceased President was dressed in an unusual one-piece suit that consisted of a pleated shirtlike top with buttoned sleeves, and plain trousers below. I suppose it was the nineteenth-century equivalent of a jumpsuit, all of one piece and probably chosen for convenience's sake. He wore no shoes or stockings, but his bony hands were sheathed in fine cloth gloves. Under his fallen lower jaw there was a very large cloth bow tie knotted butterfly fashion around his neck, a beautiful and curiously soft-looking thing, almost the sort of adornment a girl might wear.

All of the clothing and gloves must have been white originally, but now they were yellowed with age and stained by the decomposition process to a tobacco-like brown. As I have already mentioned, the lead liner itself had a cloth lining which was a faint beige color, falling down in several places. The darkness of the hair may have been due to decomposition. Apart from a few lumps of adipocere, a waxy substance that forms when body fats combine with moisture, the remains were entirely skeletal.

Then we went to work. Photographs were taken. A forensic dentist examined the teeth. With a pair of scissors I carefully cut the back of the gloves down each finger and removed all ten fingernails. I gently collected sufficient samples of hair from the President's head and his body. In the area of the feet I found several fallen toenails, including both of the nails from the great toes. We also sampled a small portion of bone from the breastbone or sternum, took a small piece of the adipocere and collected samples of the textiles from under the body that had soaked up fluids from the decomposing remains. If arsenic had been used to kill Taylor, arsenic would be present in all these things.

All the samples were placed in envelopes. Everything was divided—fingernails, hair, adipocere, bone, fabrics—so that we had two identical sets of samples. One set of specimens went to the Oak Ridge National Laboratory for analysis and the other to the Kentucky laboratory that routinely performs toxicology work for the state medical examiner.

By now it was around 4 P.M. The examination was nearly complete. The coroner's office was telephoning around Louisville to find a specialist in soldering lead. At length a man who worked with lead roofs was located and agreed to come to the office and solder the lead box shut again.

Before he arrived, Taylor's two great-great-great-great granddaughters asked to see their ancestor. This was a delicate situation. I have already described the skeletal state of the remains. Gently we described the contents of the lead box to them, and asked again: were they quite sure they wanted to look? They insisted they did; they assured us they could stand the sight. So at length the two young women were allowed to come into the room and peer into the casket containing their renowned forebear. They were enthralled, not in the least upset. I still have a photograph of them in the room, gesturing with animation and smiling excitedly.

Clare Rising, who had devoted so much time to explicating the Taylor riddle, was also permitted to come in and have a brief glimpse of the deceased President. She approached the casket with considerable hesitation and no little awe. I fixed my eyes on her and I could sense that, at that moment, she wasn't looking at a mere mass of dead bones. She was gazing on the legendary figure of history: Zachary Taylor.

The container was closed, returned to the cemetery with an American flag draped around it. It was replaced in the vault and the heavy marble lid was replaced. This time the marble was sealed with epoxy[9] that would guarantee the Taylors' privacy and repose. After this, we all went home to await the results of the laboratory analysis.

Taylor's casket is returned to the vault.

9 **epoxy:** a strong glue.

Shortly after I returned to Gainesville, the results were released by Dr. Nichols's office. They were clear and unequivocal. The amounts of arsenic found in all samples were consistent throughout. They showed that President Taylor had in his remains only the levels of arsenic consistent with any person who lived in the nineteenth-century. The levels were in every case minuscule. They could never have produced death, or even illness.

Arsenic is a remarkable and powerful poison that can kill quickly or slowly, depending on the dosage. A sudden, massive dose of arsenic could kill within hours and, if this occurs, no trace of the poison will be deposited in the hair or nails or bones of the deceased. But if the victim lives for twenty-eight to thirty hours after ingesting the arsenic, minute traces of the poison will be deposited in the hair and bones. As we all know, Zachary Taylor lived for five days after the onset of his symptoms. There was ample time for arsenic to be deposited in his system, if he had been poisoned. Our investigation demonstrated, once and for all, that he hadn't.

It is remotely possible that another poison might have been used to kill Taylor, but only arsenic would have produced the symptoms he showed before dying, and arsenic was by now conclusively out of the question. The verdict of history must be that Zachary Taylor died of natural causes. Indeed, he may have been unwittingly killed by his doctors.

In those days, cathartics and laxatives were prescribed for diarrhea, and fluids were often deliberately withheld, on the advice of doctors. A strong case might be made that the President had a fairly routine case of intestinal infection. Perhaps the vegetables and cherries he devoured had not been washed, or had been washed in contaminated water. The heat of July would have afforded a fertile breeding ground for *E. coli* germs and these, massed in millions in his gut, may have formed an army the old general could not defeat.

One minor note: we also found in the coffin several pupa cases of flies that were attracted to the dead President in that hot summer so long ago. These bold insects had paid a price for their temerity: their offspring had been buried alive with the illustrious man their parents had presumed to light upon.

The aftermath was all very anticlimactic. I learned, if I did not already know, how fickle was the fancy of the American media. Zachary Taylor the Murder Victim was news. Zachary Taylor the President who died a natural death was history, and ancient history at that. The satellite dishes were stowed, the camera lenses were capped, the generators were unplugged, the notebooks snapped shut. No more did the networks jangle my phone, wooing me with their blandishments. "Old Rough and Ready" resumed his interrupted sleep, and I returned to my modern murders unmolested. Like hoarfrost at noon, the media simply evanesced.[10]

Clare Rising finished her book on Zachary Taylor, but as far as I know it remains unpublished, despite her past literary success. She clung to her poisoning theory and did extensive additional research in the medical literature, trying to explain why, even though Taylor might have been poisoned, no poison would show up in a chemical analysis. But to my mind the death of President Taylor has been settled now, and Clare Rising is entitled to some of the credit whether she agrees or not. Without her extraordinary efforts, the mystery might have lingered indefinitely. Now it is resolved.

Zachary Taylor can take his proper place in history, as a military commander who fought hard for his country and as a President who did not shrink from his duty. His last hours may have been uncomfortable, but they were not unnatural. He was not assassinated. And, like the big soft bow tie he wore in his coffin, the old President did have a gentler side.

It was Zachary Taylor who coined the term "First Lady." He used these words to describe Dolly Madison at her funeral in 1849: "She will never be forgotten, because she was truly our first lady for a half century." This sincere piece of gallantry is among his smaller monuments. It came from Zachary Taylor's own heart—a heart that was gone, together with the storm and strife it struggled to master, long before the old President and I met. ∽

---

10 **evanesced:** disappeared.

# RESPONDING TO CLUSTER THREE

## HOW DO YOU SOLVE A MYSTERY?

## Thinking Skill  LOGICAL THINKING

1. Sometimes facts can be interpreted two different ways. With the facts presented in "Arsenic and Old Rough and Ready," use **logical thinking** to determine which conclusion you think is correct: William Maples' assertion that Zachary Taylor was not murdered, or Clare Rising's assertion that Taylor could have been poisoned.

2. Compare William Maples' methods in "Arsenic and Old Rough and Ready" to Sherlock Holmes' methods in *The Dying Detective*. Use a **Venn diagram** similar to the one below to show the similarities and differences in their logic.

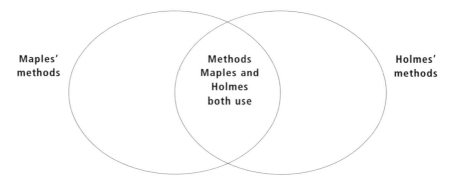

Maples'
methods

Methods
Maples and
Holmes
both use

Holmes'
methods

3. Do you prefer fiction or nonfiction mysteries? (*The Dying Detective* and "A Poison That Leaves No Trace" are examples of fiction mysteries; "Arsenic and Old Rough and Ready" is an example of a nonfiction mystery.) Explain your answer.

### Writing Activity: What Maks a Good Detective?

Create a profile of your own fictional sleuth, drawing from the detectives you have read about in this book, or from other sources such as movies, television, or books.

### A Strong Profile

• describes a person's interests, traits, skills, mannerisms, personality, etc.

• is short; think of a sketch rather than a full-color portrait

• focuses on character traits that make the person unique

# CLUSTER FOUR

## Thinking On Your Own

Thinking Skill   SYNTHESIZING

# Lamb to the Slaughter

ROALD DAHL

The room was warm and clean, the curtains drawn, the two table lamps alight—hers and the one by the empty chair opposite. On the sideboard behind her, two tall glasses, soda water, whiskey. Fresh ice cubes in the Thermos bucket.

Mary Maloney was waiting for her husband to come home from work.

Now and again she would glance up at the clock, but without anxiety, merely to please herself with the thought that each minute gone by made it nearer the time when he would come. There was a slow smiling air about her, and about everything she did. The drop of the head as she bent over her sewing was curiously tranquil. Her skin—for this was her sixth month with child—had acquired a wonderful translucent quality, the mouth was soft, and the eyes, with their new placid look, seemed larger, darker than before.

When the clock said ten minutes to five, she began to listen, and a few moments later, punctually as always, she heard the tires on the gravel outside, and the car door slamming, the footsteps passing the window, the key turning in the lock. She laid aside her sewing, stood up, and went forward to kiss him as he came in.

"Hullo darling," she said.

"Hullo," he answered.

She took his coat and hung it in the closet. Then she walked over and made the drinks, a strongish one for him, a weak one for herself; and soon she was back again in her chair with the sewing, and he in the other, opposite, holding the tall glass with both his hands, rocking it so the ice cubes tinkled against the side.

BREEDING CHAMPIONS
1977-78 Barry Castle.

For her, this was always a blissful time of day. She knew he didn't want to speak much until the first drink was finished, and she, on her side, was content to sit quietly, enjoying his company after the long hours alone in the house. She loved to luxuriate in the presence of this man, and to feel—almost as a sunbather feels the sun—that warm male glow that came out of him to her when they were alone together. She loved him for the way he sat loosely in a chair, for the way he came in a door, or moved slowly across the room with long strides. She loved the intent, far look in his eyes when they rested on her, the funny shape of the mouth, and especially the way he remained silent about his tiredness, sitting still with himself until the whiskey had taken some of it away.

"Tired, darling?"

"Yes," he said. "I'm tired." And as he spoke, he did an unusual thing. He lifted his glass and drained it in one swallow although there was still half of it, at least half of it, left. She wasn't really watching him, but she knew what he had done because she heard the ice cubes falling back against the bottom of the empty glass when he lowered his arm. He paused a moment, leaning forward in the chair, then he got up and went slowly over to fetch himself another.

"I'll get it!" she cried, jumping up.

"Sit down," he said.

When he came back, she noticed that the new drink was dark amber with the quantity of whiskey in it.

"Darling, shall I get your slippers?"

"No."

She watched him as he began to sip the dark yellow drink, and she could see little oily swirls in the liquid because it was so strong.

"I think it's a shame," she said, "that when a policeman gets to be as senior as you, they keep him walking about on his feet all day long."

He didn't answer, so she bent her head again and went on with her sewing; but each time he lifted the drink to his lips, she heard the ice cubes clinking against the side of the glass.

"Darling," she said. "Would you like me to get you some cheese? I haven't made any supper yet because it's Thursday."

"No," he said.

"If you're too tired to eat out," she went on, "it's still not too late. There's plenty of meat and stuff in the freezer, and you can have it right here and not even move out of the chair."

Her eyes waited on him for an answer, a smile, a little nod, but he made no sign.

"Anyway," she went on, "I'll get you some cheese and crackers first."

"I don't want it," he said.

She moved uneasily in her chair, the large eyes still watching his face. "But you *must* have supper. I can easily do it here. I'd like to do it. We can have lamb chops. Or pork. Anything you want. Everything's in the freezer."

"Forget it," he said.

"But darling, you must eat! I'll fix it anyway, and then you can have it or not, as you like."

"Sit down," he said. "Just for a minute, sit down."

It wasn't till then that she began to get frightened.

"Go on," he said, "Sit down."

She lowered herself back slowly into the chair, watching him all the time with those large, bewildered eyes. He had finished the second drink and was staring down into the glass, frowning.

"Listen," he said. "I've got something to tell you."

"What is it, darling? What's the matter?"

He had now become absolutely motionless, and he kept his head down so that the light from the lamp beside him fell across the upper part of his face, leaving the chin and mouth in shadow. She noticed there was a little muscle moving near the corner of his left eye.

"This is going to be a bit of a shock to you, I'm afraid," he said. "But I've thought about it a good deal and I've decided the only thing to do is tell you right away. I hope you won't blame me too much."

And he told her. It didn't take long, four or five minutes at most, and she sat very still through it all, watching him with a kind of dazed horror as he went further and further away from her with each word.

"So there it is," he added. "And I know it's kind of a bad time to be telling you, but there simply wasn't any other way. Of course I'll give you money and see you're looked after. But there needn't really be any fuss. I hope not anyway. It wouldn't be very good for my job."

Her first instinct was not to believe any of it, to reject it all. It occurred to her that perhaps he hadn't even spoken, that she herself had imagined the whole thing. Maybe, if she went about her business and acted as though she hadn't been listening, then later, when she sort of woke up again, she might find none of it had ever happened.

"I'll get the supper," she managed to whisper, and this time he didn't stop her.

When she walked across the room she couldn't feel her feet touching the floor. She couldn't feel anything at all—except a slight nausea and a desire to vomit. Everything was automatic now—down the steps to the cellar, the light switch, the deep freeze, the hand inside the cabinet taking hold of the first object it met. She lifted it out, and looked at it. It was wrapped in paper, so she took off the paper and looked at it again.

A leg of lamb.

All right then, they would have lamb for supper. She carried it upstairs, holding the thin bone-end of it with both her hands, and as she went through the living-room, she saw him standing over by the window with his back to her, and she stopped.

"For God's sake," he said, hearing her, but not turning round. "Don't make supper for me. I'm going out."

At that point, Mary Maloney simply walked up behind him and without any pause she swung the big frozen leg of lamb high in the air and brought it down as hard as she could on the back of his head.

She might just as well have hit him with a steel club.

She stepped back a pace, waiting, and the funny thing was that he remained standing there for at least four or five seconds, gently swaying. Then he crashed to the carpet.

The violence of the crash, the noise, the small table overturning, helped bring her out of the shock. She came out slowly, feeling cold and surprised, and she stood for a while blinking at the body, still holding the ridiculous piece of meat tight with both hands.

All right, she told herself. So I've killed him.

It was extraordinary, now, how clear her mind became all of a sudden. She began thinking very fast. As the wife of a detective, she knew quite well what the penalty would be. That was fine. It made no difference to her. In fact, it would be a relief. On the other hand, what about the child? What were the laws about murderers with unborn children? Did they kill them both—mother and child? Or did they wait until the tenth month? What did they do?

Mary Maloney didn't know. And she certainly wasn't prepared to take a chance.

She carried the meat into the kitchen, placed it in a pan, turned the oven on high and shoved it inside. Then she washed her hands and ran upstairs to the bedroom. She sat down before the mirror, tidied her hair, and touched up her lips and face. She tried a smile. It came out rather peculiar. She tried again.

"Hullo Sam," she said brightly, aloud.

The voice sounded peculiar too.

"I want some potatoes please, Sam. Yes, and I think a can of peas." That was better. Both the smile and the voice were coming out better now. She rehearsed it several times more. Then she ran downstairs, took her coat, went out the back door, down the garden, into the street.

It wasn't six o'clock yet and the lights were still on in the grocery shop.

"Hullo Sam," she said brightly, smiling at the man behind the counter.

"Why, good evening, Mrs. Maloney. How're you?"

"I want some potatoes please, Sam. Yes, and I think a can of peas."

The man turned and reached up behind him on the shelf for the peas.

"Patrick's decided he's tired and doesn't want to eat out tonight," she told him. "We usually go out Thursdays, you know, and now he's caught me without any vegetables in the house."

"Then how about meat, Mrs. Maloney?"

"No, I've got meat, thanks. I got a nice leg of lamb from the freezer."

"Oh."

"I don't much like cooking it frozen, Sam, but I'm taking a chance on it this time. You think it'll be all right?"

"Personally," the grocer said, "I don't believe it makes any difference. You want these Idaho potatoes?"

"Oh yes, that'll be fine. Two of those."

"Anything else?" The grocer cocked his head on one side, looking at her pleasantly. "How about afterwards? What you going to give him for afterwards?"

"Well—what would you suggest, Sam?"

The man glanced around his shop. "How about a nice big slice of cheesecake? I know he likes that."

"Perfect," she said. "He loves it."

And when it was all wrapped and she had paid, she put on her brightest smile and said, "Thank you, Sam. Goodnight."

"Goodnight, Mrs. Maloney. And thank *you.*"

And now, she told herself as she hurried back, all she was doing now, she was returning home to her husband and he was waiting for his supper; and she must cook it good, and make it tasty as possible because the poor man was tired; and if, when she entered the house, she happened to find anything unusual, or tragic, or terrible, then naturally it would be a shock and she'd become frantic with grief and horror. Mind you, she wasn't *expecting* to find anything. She was just going home with the vegetables. Mrs. Patrick Maloney going home with the vegetables on Thursday evening to cook supper for her husband.

That's the way, she told herself. Do everything right and natural. Keep things absolutely natural and there'll be no need for any acting at all.

Therefore, when she entered the kitchen by the back door, she was humming a little tune to herself and smiling.

"Patrick!" She called. "How are you, darling!"

She put the parcel down on the table and went through into the living room; and when she saw him lying there on the floor with his legs doubled up and one arm twisted back underneath his body, it really was rather a shock. All the old love and longing for him welled up inside her, and she ran over to him, knelt down beside him, and began to cry her heart out. It was easy. No acting was necessary.

A few minutes later she got up and went to the phone. She knew the number of the police station, and when the man at the other end answered, she cried to him, "Quick! Come quick! Patrick's dead!"

"Who's speaking?"

"Mrs. Maloney. Mrs. Patrick Maloney."

"You mean Patrick Maloney's dead?"

"I think so," she sobbed. "He's lying on the floor and I think he's dead."

"Be right over," the man said.

The car came very quickly, and when she opened the front door, two policemen walked in. She knew them both—she knew nearly all the men at the precinct—and she fell right into Jack Noonan's arms, weeping hysterically. He put her gently into a chair, then went over to join the other one, who was called O'Malley, kneeling by the body.

"Is he dead?" she cried.

"I'm afraid he is. What happened?"

Briefly, she told her story about going out to the grocer and coming back to find him on the floor. While she was talking, crying and talking, Noonan discovered a small patch of congealed blood on the dead man's head. He showed it to O'Malley, who got up at once and hurried to the phone.

Soon, other men began to come into the house. First a doctor, then two detectives, one of whom she knew by name. Later, a police photographer arrived and took pictures, and a man who knew about fingerprints. There was a great deal of whispering and muttering beside the corpse, and the detectives kept asking her a lot of questions. But they always treated her kindly. She told her story again, this time right from the beginning, when Patrick had come in, and she was sewing, and he was tired, so tired he hadn't wanted to go out for supper. She told how she'd put the meat in the oven—"it's there now, cooking"—and how she'd slipped out to the grocer for vegetables, and come back to find him lying on the floor.

"Which grocer?" one of the detectives asked.

She told him, and he turned and whispered something to the other detective, who immediately went outside into the street.

In fifteen minutes he was back with a page of notes, and there was more whispering, and through her sobbing she heard a few of the whispered phrases—". . . acted quite normal . . . very cheerful . . . wanted to give him a good supper . . . peas . . . cheesecake . . . impossible that she . . ."

After a while, the photographer and the doctor departed, and two other men came in and took the corpse away on a stretcher. Then the fingerprint man went away. The two detectives remained, and so did the two policemen. They were exceptionally nice to her, and Jack Noonan asked if she wouldn't rather go somewhere else, to her sister's house perhaps, or to his own wife, who would take care of her and put her up for the night.

No, she said. She didn't feel she could move even a yard at the moment. Would they mind awfully if she stayed just where she was until she felt better? She didn't feel too good at the moment, she really didn't.

Then hadn't she better lie down on the bed? Jack Noonan asked.

No, she said. She'd like to stay right where she was, in this chair. A little later perhaps, when she felt better, she would move.

So they left her there while they went about their business, searching the house. Occasionally one of the detectives asked her another question. Sometimes Jack Noonan spoke at her gently as he passed by. Her husband, he told her, had been killed by a blow on the back of the head administered with a heavy blunt instrument, almost certainly a large piece of metal. They were looking for the weapon. The murderer may have taken it with him, but on the other hand he may've thrown it away or hidden it somewhere on the premises.

"It's the old story," he said. "Get the weapon, and you've got the man."

Later, one of the detectives came up and sat beside her. Did she know, he asked, of anything in the house that could've been used as the weapon? Would she mind having a look around to see if anything was missing—a very big spanner, for example, or a heavy metal vase.

They didn't have any heavy metal vases, she said.

"Or a big spanner?"

She didn't think they had a big spanner. But there might be some things like that in the garage.

The search went on. She knew that there were other policemen in the garden all around the house. She could hear their footsteps on the gravel outside, and sometimes she saw the flash of a torch through a chink in the curtains. It began to get late, nearly nine she noticed by the clock on the mantel. The four men searching the rooms seemed to be growing weary, a trifle exasperated.

"Jack," she said, the next time Sergeant Noonan went by. "Would you mind giving me a drink?"

"Sure, I'll give you a drink. You mean this whiskey?"

"Yes please. But just a small one. It might make me feel better."

He handed her the glass.

"Why don't you have one yourself," she said. "You must be awfully tired. Please do. You've been very good to me."

"Well," he answered. "It's not strictly allowed, but I might take just a drop to keep me going."

One by one the others came in and were persuaded to take a little nip of whiskey. They stood around rather awkwardly with the drinks in their hands, uncomfortable in her presence, trying to say consoling things to her. Sergeant Noonan wandered into the kitchen, came out quickly and said, "Look, Mrs. Maloney. You know that oven of yours is still on, and the meat still inside."

"Oh *dear* me!" she cried. "So it is!"

"I better turn it off for you, hadn't I?"

"Will you do that, Jack? Thank you so much."

When the sergeant returned the second time, she looked at him with her large, dark, tearful eyes. "Jack Noonan," she said.

"Yes?"

"Would you do me a small favor—you and these others?"

"We can try, Mrs. Maloney."

"Well," she said. "Here you all are, and good friends of dear Patrick's too, and helping to catch the man who killed him. You must be terribly hungry by now because it's long past your suppertime, and I know Patrick would never forgive me, God bless his soul, if I allowed you to remain in his house without offering you decent hospitality. Why don't you eat up that lamb that's in the oven? It'll be cooked just right by now."

"Wouldn't dream of it," Sergeant Noonan said.

"Please," she begged. "Please eat it. Personally I couldn't touch a thing, certainly not what's been in the house when he was here. But it's all right for you. It'd be a favor to me if you'd eat it up. Then you can go on with your work again afterwards."

There was a good deal of hesitating among the four policemen, but they were clearly hungry, and in the end they were persuaded to go into the kitchen and help themselves. The woman stayed where she was, listening to them through the open door, and she could hear them speaking among themselves, their voices thick and sloppy because their mouths were full of meat.

"Have some more, Charlie?"

"No. Better not finish it."

"She *wants* us to finish it. She said so. Be doing her a favor."

"Okay then. Give me some more."

"That's a hell of a big club the guy must've used to hit poor Patrick," one of them was saying. "The doc says his skull was smashed all to pieces just like from a sledgehammer."

"That's why it ought to be easy to find."

"Exactly what I say."

"Whoever done it, they're not going to be carrying a thing like that around with them longer than they need."

One of them belched.

"Personally, I think it's right here on the premises."

"Probably right under our very noses. What you think, Jack?" And in the other room, Mary Maloney began to giggle. ❧

# This Way Nobody Gets the Blame

LESLEY GRANT-ADAMSON

**T**his way," he said, "nobody gets the blame."

Ella gave him a teasing look, which he missed because he was striding along, quite quickly considering how much he had to carry. But he'd sounded so proud she couldn't resist saying: "It was very clever of you to work it all out, Phil."

He took the remark seriously. "You too, Ella. It's just as much your plan as mine."

"Well, whoever it belongs to, let's hope it works."

This time he stopped and looked hard at her. "You haven't spotted a flaw? I mean, if there's anything not quite right now's the time to . . . ."

"No, no, it's perfect."

"You're sure?"

"Honestly. It's foolproof."

"And it's as good as done." He began to walk again, his waterproof jacket rustling.

The path narrowed and Ella trailed behind. Over to the right the sea heaved against a rocky shore. For the rest there was an empty hinterland, with sunlight fading on granite walls enclosing salty fields.

Philip urged her on with an impatient toss of his head, but she thought it added a touch of normality if she were dawdling, so she didn't hurry.

"Come on." He took up a studied, relaxed stance while waiting for her. He was a terribly unconvincing actor, his irritation undisguised. She'd experienced a lot of it lately. Nobody would have dreamed the whole mess was his fault and not hers.

*"I am the innocent victim,"* she thought, dreamily, as she watched the waves rushing to destruction.

She turned the dreamy look into a smile as she drew nearer to her husband. "I'm trying to look natural, Phil. We shouldn't dash as though we expect every wave to be the last."

"I don't remember rehearsing this dithering when we did our trial runs."

She winced at the unfortunate word, trial, but Philip appeared not to notice and strode on. After a few paces he ushered her past him so that from then on he was following her, or rather he was shepherding her down the path.

They passed the kink where a big stone had broken free and the surface was slippery. Ella skipped swiftly on but she heard her husband's boots slide on the scree.[1] He was fond of those boots, he'd had them for years, but there'd been too many slips for her to believe they gripped well.

Philip hadn't proved sure-footed in other, figurative, ways either. He'd made a mess of his business and a worse one in borrowing to wriggle out of trouble. And then he'd done the very silly thing.

Like everything else about him, his mistake, his crime, was unoriginal. It used to be called borrowing from Peter to pay Paul, but now there were bleaker ways of describing it. Misappropriation, fraud, or embezzlement. They came to the same thing: he'd stolen money.

"We're in a fix," he'd admitted to Ella the day he told her about the huge debt, the investor who'd be plundered, and the sham their lives had become.

"You mean we'll have to sell Silver Acre?"

She loved the old house, its cozy position in a hollow overlooking the sea, and the status that being its owner conferred on her. She'd never been comfortable before. Her childhood had been poor, and in the years when Philip was building his business they'd scraped by in a bungalow on a modern estate. At Silver Acre she felt truly at home for the first time in her life.

When he didn't answer her question, she'd asked another one: "Who else knows about this?"

"Nobody."

---

1 **scree:** loose stones lying on a slope or at the base of a cliff.

"Not even Heidi?"

"Not even her."

Heidi was his assistant, an Austrian woman with bright blue eyes and a singsong accent. At one time Ella suspected she was rather closer to him than that, but Philip had persuaded her not.

"Is there nothing else we can do?"

He gave a bitter laugh. "Not to save the house. We offered it as security and the bank will take it."

"Are we going bankrupt?"

He spoke flatly, as though explaining to someone especially dim. "*We're* going to be bankrupt and *I'm* probably going to be in prison."

"But . . ."

"But what? Don't you think I've thought all around this, before I decided I had to tell you?"

"Yes, I'm sure you did."

It had always been his way to do things and tell her afterwards. She used to protest at him shutting her out but it made no difference because it was his nature.

For a second she was so angry with him that she didn't care whether he went to prison or not. It would be what he deserved for wrecking her life as well as his own, she thought; but the thought was very brief. "There must be a way," she said.

And she saw from his face that he thought so, too. Before long they were plotting.

The path turned into rugged steps. Ella climbed down easily. On the first visit she'd found it tricky but they'd tramped this route half a dozen times since that evening of plotting. If anyone had cared to look they would have noticed that the couple from Silver Acre liked to go fishing below the cliffs some evenings.

But no one would have guessed that one evening their car was to be abandoned where they usually parked it, near the start of the path. Or that a van had been bought especially for them to flee in and lay hidden in a barn on the edge of their land. Or that in its glove box were false passports. Or that Philip had rounded up what was left of the money, a substantial amount as long as no debts were honored, and had transferred it abroad.

Where the steps met the rocks Ella paused once again and gazed around. A wave frothed towards her. The lower step was awash, her boots and ankles drenched.

Behind her Philip said: "You see? If you hadn't been hanging about we'd have been over without getting wet."

He splashed past her and hoisted himself up on to the rocks. "Come on," he shouted back. "Give me a hand with this."

Ella leaped across while the water was receding, perched on her usual toe hold and reached the top of the rock. A buffeting wind was coming from the west. Waves were jagged white lines when they were far out, but whisked into fury near the shore. With a terrible sucking, the water snatched what it could from the land.

While Philip battled to position their rods, she stayed where she was. They'd hoped for a lively sea, to give credence to the idea that they'd been swept away and drowned. So far, luck was with them.

She couldn't just stand there, watching him. He seemed to be having trouble with her rod, and he gestured for her to help. For a moment she was rooted. Then she darted forward, keen to get it done.

Ella sprang at him and sent him over the edge. He had no chance, in those slippery boots of his. She didn't hear him cry out, but she saw his astonishment. In the instant before she made contact, he'd been turning towards her, arm outstretched. Her first thought, as he disappeared into the spray, was that she was fortunate to have avoided his clutching hand. If he'd moved more quickly, or if she'd been slower, he would certainly have got a grip on her sleeve and she could have plunged into the sea.

Alone, she followed the escape route along the cliff top. Rain was blowing on the wind and the light was as poor as she'd hoped. Any lighter and she might be recognized, any darker and she'd need a torch. Soon the waves were turbulent ghosts on a black sea. She cut inland.

At last she drew close to the barn. Its door was rattling in the wind. *"Philip ought to have made it secure,"* she thought crossly. *"Supposing it had blown open and someone had noticed the van?"*

Inside the barn it was totally dark. She felt the van's bumper against her leg and squeezed round to the driver's door. As she opened it, everything collapsed in a whirl of confusion.

A woman in the passenger seat was gabbling at her in a singsong voice, pawing at her, "Oh, Philip, I thought you'd never come! How did it go? Did she suspect anything? It must have been absolutely terrible for you . . ." ❧

# Invitation to a Murder

JOSH PACHTER

The envelope was edged in black.

Curious, Branigan set the rest of his stack of mail aside and reached for the jeweled souvenir dagger he used as a letter opener. He slit the envelope open carefully, and slid out a square of heavy cream-colored notepaper.

It, too, was black-rimmed.

It was a formal, embossed announcement and the raised letters read:

Eleanor Madeline Abbott
Announces the Impending
Murder
Of Her Husband, Gregory Eliot Abbott,
At Their Home,
217A West 86th Street, New York City, New York,
Between the Hours of
Nine Thirty and Eleven o'clock
On the Evening of December 16, 1971.
You Are Cordially Invited to Attend.

Branigan read through the invitation twice, then set it down on his desk and picked up the envelope it had arrived in. Heavy, cream-colored, black-bordered. Addressed in a precise feminine hand to *Chief Inspector Lawrence A. Branigan, New York Police Department, 240 Centre Street, New York, New York*. No zip code. No return address. Postmarked New York City.

Branigan picked up the announcement and read it again. Eleanor Abbott, he mused. Mrs. Eleanor Madeline Abbott . . .

He reached for his telephone and began dialing.

It was still snowing when Branigan walked up the brownstone's eight steps and rang the bell. The door was opened almost immediately by a large man in butler's livery, black from head to toe except for the thin white triangle of his shirtfront.

"Inspector Branigan?" he asked, his voice surprisingly soft.

Branigan, nodding, pulled the black-rimmed invitation from his overcoat pocket and handed it over. Behind the butler, all he could see was a dimly lit corridor stretching back into darkness.

"Thank you, sir," the man said. "All the others have already arrived. Would you follow me, please?"

*The others?* Branigan thought, as he stepped into the house. *All the others?*

Halfway down the corridor, before a large wooden door, they stopped. The butler twisted the ornate brass knob and pushed the door open. "In here, sir," he said. "Mrs. Abbott is expecting you. May I take your coat?"

The room was dim, too. Like the corridor, like the butler, like the night. Thick damask curtains hid what might have been windows; subdued lighting trickled down from small panels set into the ceiling.

It was a large, plain room. No rugs or carpeting on the simple parquet floor, no paintings, nothing personal hanging from the dark, gloomy walls. There was nothing extra in the room, nothing decorative. Every item, every piece of furniture, was there because it was functional, because it was needed.

Like the double bed standing with its head flush to the far wall.

There was a man on the bed, propped up almost to a sitting position. His body was invisible, swathed to the neck in heavy blankets, but his wrinkled white face almost shone through the dimness.

Gregory Abbott.

At first Branigan thought he was too late, thought Abbott was already dead: the pale gray eyes, half covered by deeply creased lids, stared emptily across the room; the ravaged face, wreathed by wisps of snowy hair, was perfectly still. No smile of welcome, no frown of disapproval crossed the old man's thin, bloodless lips.

Then he noticed the slight rise and fall of the blankets, and separated the faint sound of labored breathing from the steady ticking of the clock that hung on the wall several feet above Abbott's head.

Branigan sighed with relief, and looked away.

To his right, a high-backed chair stood against the side wall. A young woman was poised lightly on the edge of the chair, her hands folded delicately in her lap. She wore a long black gown, simple and yet striking, set off by a single strand of pearls around her neck and a sparkling diamond on the fourth finger of her left hand. Branigan had learned that Eleanor Abbott was an attractive woman. He saw now that she was beautiful: as beautiful and, somehow, as cold as the December night outside.

Across the room from her, a dozen identical chairs stood side by side. The seat closest to Branigan was empty, obviously his, but each of the others was occupied. And, even in the dimness of the room, he recognized the eleven faces that were turned toward him, waiting.

Ryan was there, from the Los Angeles Police Department, and DiNapoli from San Francisco, both officers he had worked with in the past. There was Coszyck, who ran a local detective agency; Huber, an insurance investigator from Boston he had worked with once before; Braun, a private eye based in Cleveland, whose picture he had recently seen featured in a national news magazine. There was Devereaux, a Federal District Court justice from New Orleans; Gould, a St. Louis appellate court judge; even Walter Fox, "the old Fox," as he was known, just retired from the bench of the United States Supreme Court. Maunders, Detroit's crusading District Attorney, was there, and Szambel from Pittsburgh, and Carpenter, who had left Szambel's staff to become D.A. of Baltimore.

The eleven men looked at him closely, and Branigan could see that most of them recognized him, too.

They were fourteen people in all, lining the walls of the nearly dark, nearly quiet room, the silence broken only by Gregory Abbott's uneven breathing and by the inexorable ticking of the clock.

Finally, Branigan's eyes rested on the plain deal table in the center of the room, and on the five objects that sat on its surface: a long-bladed kitchen knife, a thin strand of wire with a wooden grip attached to each end, a length of iron pipe, an amber bottle labeled with a grinning skull and crossbones, and a revolver that glinted dully in the dim light of the room.

*It was Miss Scarlet,* Branigan found himself thinking. *In the conservatory, with the candelabra.*

The image should have been funny, but it wasn't. It frightened him, frightened him deeply, and he was not sure why.

He looked back at the woman in the black gown.

She was smiling at him, and Branigan saw that she knew what he was thinking.

*She's playing with us,* he thought. *She set it up like this, and now she's playing with us. It's just a game to her.*

A game with the highest stakes imaginable. A game where the life of the old man in the double bed goes to the winner.

*Okay,* Branigan thought. *Okay, I'm ready.*

He took a step forward, into the room, and eased the door shut behind him.

Eleanor Abbott stood up. A lock of hair drifted down across her eyes as she rose, and she carelessly brushed it back with the tips of her fingers.

"Good evening, Inspector Branigan," she said. "If you'll take your seat, we can get started." She spoke softly, pleasantly, almost in a whisper, yet her voice carried firmly across the room.

It was a good voice, Branigan decided. It suited her.

He moved to the empty chair at the end of the row of twelve, and sat.

"Thank you," she said. "And thank you for coming. I want to thank *all* of you for being here tonight. I knew that *you* would come, Inspector, and you, Mr. Coszyck, since both of you live and work right here in New York. And I was confident that my invitation would pique your curiosities, Mr. Huber and Mr. Carpenter, enough to get you to make the trip to town. But most of the rest of you, though, I have to admit that your presence comes as a very welcome surprise. Some of you had to travel great distances to get here; your dedication to the protection of human life impresses me. And especially you, Mr. Justice Fox, I want to—"

"Come off it, young lady!" Fox said hoarsely. "Why I showed up here tonight doesn't make a bit of difference. What I want to know is why you sent me that—that incredible invitation!"

"Why did I invite you?" She smiled at him, the same warm smile she had already used once on Branigan. "I'm not a liar, sir. I invited you here—I invited all twelve of you gentlemen, twelve of this country's most eminent and respected legal and law-enforcement minds—I invited you here to witness a murder."

She paused, then—paused dramatically, Branigan realized with a start. He glanced down the row of his colleagues' faces and saw eleven pairs of eyes fixed, unwavering, on Eleanor Abbott. Only the old man in the bed was not looking at her; his blank eyes never moved from an invisible spot on the door across the room.

"But first," the woman went on, "I want to give you just a little bit of personal history. I was born in Philadelphia in 1945, and—"

"You were born on *Thursday*, September the thirteenth, 1945," Braun broke in, "and not in Philadelphia, you were born in Essington, which is a few miles outside the city limits. I guarantee that every one of us has looked very carefully into your personal history, Mrs. Abbott, so why don't you just get to the point?"

"The point," she said slowly. "I *am* getting to the point, Mr. Braun. I know that you've all done your homework, and I hope you'll all be willing to let me tell this in my own way."

She looked around her and smiled again. "You can see that this means quite a lot to me. I'll try not to take up more of your time than I have to."

*That's one for her,* Branigan thought. *This is her party, and she knows it.*

"Go ahead, Mrs. Abbott," he said. "Do it your way."

She turned to him and nodded and said "Thank you." Her leaving off the "Inspector" at the end of it made it a personal statement, and he thought for a moment that he would like to call her Eleanor.

And then she turned again, faced the old man in the bed and looked through him.

"I came to New York about five years ago," she said, "when I was twenty-one. The first two years I was here, I must have lived in half a dozen different tiny little apartments around town; I worked at three or four different silly little jobs. I made sandwiches in a delicatessen. I was a secretary for a few weeks, and not a very good one. I worked in a record store. One time I applied to a couple of the airlines, trying to get into stewardess school, but none of them were hiring.

"Three years ago, I was waiting tables at a little Italian restaurant down in the Village; Greenwich Village. One night—I can tell you what night it was; it was October nineteenth, 1968—that night, Gregory came in for dinner with some woman he'd been going out with and another couple."

She closed her eyes, and it was a moment before she went on. "I served them their dinner, they ate, they left, I never really noticed them. Then, a few hours later, I got off work, and Gregory was waiting for me outside. I don't know what he did with his girlfriend, but there he was. It was just like a movie: Gregory Abbott's got six million dollars in the bank, and he's leaning up against a parking meter with his grubby old hat on the back of his head and a beautiful bunch of flowers he'd picked up somewhere, at that hour, in his arms, and he's waiting for *me.* That was Gregory. That was the way he was.

"We got married six months later, a year and a half ago. It turned out he loved me." She opened her eyes and faced them. "It turned out I loved him, too."

"He was thirty-five years older than you were!"

"He still *is* thirty-five years older than I am. I thought it didn't matter." She let her eyes close again before going on. "I was wrong," she said. "It does matter. One year ago today, Gregory and I were staying with some friends in Aspen. I ski very badly, Gregory hadn't skied before at all, but they were very good friends and we were having a wonderful time. Late in the afternoon, Gregory said he felt practiced enough to try a run down one of the more advanced slopes. I—I remember thinking it wasn't a very good idea, but he was so full of energy, so full of life. . . ."

The room seemed subtly brighter, Branigan thought, and before he could wonder why he knew it was her face. *She looks as white as the snow must have been,* he told himself, and then was irritated by the thought.

"He fell," Eleanor Abbott said. "He lost his balance halfway down and fell. I was coming down behind him, I saw it happen, and there was nothing I could do. We got the ski patrol to bring him down the rest of the way. They had an ambulance waiting, and I rode to the hospital with him. The doctors said he had a massive coronary. He was in critical condition for more than a week.

"He pulled through, though. He survived." The color flushed back into her face, a violent red. "If you can call the way it left him survival. He's totally paralyzed. He can't see or hear. After it happened, I spent two hysterical months trying to get him to blink an eye for me, to show me it's just something gone wrong with his body, to tell me that somewhere in there *he* is okay. There was no response. The doctors tell me he is no longer able to think."

"Mrs. Abbott," Maunders said, softly.

She looked up. "It's been a year, now. He doesn't get any better or any worse. The doctors tell me there is no chance that he will ever recover, they hold out no hope at all. They *do* think, though, that with the proper medical care and treatment they can keep his *body* alive for ten more years, or even longer."

She said it bitterly, angrily, and for an instant Branigan found that he shared her anger.

"I'm not going to let them do that," she said. "Gregory Abbott is dead. That—that *thing* in the bed there is not my husband. My husband died a year ago today."

There was something new in her voice now, layered over the bitterness: something insistent, almost hypnotic. They stared at her, all of them, as motionless as the empty old man in the double bed.

"I loved my husband," she told them. "Out of my love for him, I feel that there's one last thing I have to do for him. I have to put an end to that horror the doctors say is still alive, that terrible thing that *I* know is Gregory's corpse. I want to give him what the doctors have refused to let him have, this last year. I want to let him rest."

"And of course, you don't care about the six million dollars," Gould snapped at her. It was, somehow, a shocking statement, and it seemed natural for her just to gaze at him in silence, until he backed away from it and said, "No. No, I guess you don't. I'm sorry."

"The money is already mine, Mr. Gould," she said. "Gregory can't use it any more. And you're right, I don't care about it. The only thing I care about right now is my husband. That's why I'm going to kill him."

*There,* Branigan thought. *That's it. That's what I came to hear her say.* And then he frowned, asking himself why, now that he had heard her say it, the words surprised him.

"Just a minute, now," Ryan began, but she smiled at him and cut him off. "I know, Captain," she said gently. "I'm talking about murder, and murder is against the law. That's the *second* reason I invited the twelve of you here tonight: I wanted to give the law a fair chance to stop me. If you can, if you can keep what I intend to happen here from happening, then I give you my word that I'll never try anything like this again; I'll leave Gregory's body to his doctors and let them do what they like with it. But I want to warn you: you are not going to stop me. I am going to murder the miniscule amount of my husband the doctors have succeeded in keeping alive, tonight in this room, within the next hour. It's now"—she turned her head to glance at the clock on the wall—"It is now ten o'clock. By eleven, in one hour, even the doctors will agree that Gregory Abbott is dead."

No one spoke. The woman in the long black gown sat down to silence, except for the whisper of her husband's breathing and the steady ticking of the clock hanging over his bed.

The twelve men looked at each other, at Eleanor Abbott, at the old man. They sat without speaking, spellbound, waiting, not quite sure what it was they should be doing, not at all sure there was anything they *could* do to prevent the murder they had been invited to witness.

They sat until ten minutes had passed, until Eleanor Abbott rose, walked quickly to the table of weapons in the center of the room, and picked up the amber bottle of poison.

Then they moved, and strong hands grabbed her from both sides before she could step away from the table. Branigan pulled the bottle away from her, and he and Coszyck led her back to her chair. She sat willingly, and they went back to their own seats without a word.

*What is she up to?* Branigan thought. *She can't possibly imagine we'll let her get near him. What does she think is going on?*

At 10:20, she rose again. She was halfway to the table when Branigan and Coszyck stopped her, turned around, and put her back in her chair.

This time they stayed with her, one on either side.

And still the old man's breathing and the ticking of the clock were the only sounds in the room. There was a moment when Carpenter put a hand to his mouth and coughed softly: Eleanor Abbott seemed not to notice and Gregory Abbott stared ahead vacantly; most of the rest of them glared at Carpenter, and he turned away, embarrassed.

At 10:30, Huber jumped up and moved impatiently to the old man's bedside. He went down to his hands and knees and carefully examined the floor beneath the bed and the bed itself. As he straightened up, dusting off the legs of his trousers, Braun and Devereaux looked at each other and got up and joined him. They ranged themselves around the three open sides of the bed, watching Abbott and his wife and the clock uneasily.

At 10:40, Eleanor Abbott suddenly stood, but Branigan and Coszyck clamped firm hands on her shoulders and forced her back into her chair.

Again, not a word was said.

The thin red second hand of the clock swept around and around as the minute hand labored slowly up the numbered face. DiNapoli glanced from the clock to his wrist, then quickly back at the clock. He scowled impatiently and adjusted his watch so the two timepieces were synchronized.

At 10:50 Maunders and Fox stood up together, grim-faced, and stepped to the table of weapons. The old Fox, his arthritic fingers quivering slightly, picked up the revolver. He broke open the cylinder, emptied out the cartridges and pocketed them, snapped the cylinder shut and placed the gun back on the table.

At 10:55, Branigan and Coszyck rested their hands lightly on Mrs. Abbott's shoulders.

Devereaux, at Abbott's bedside, pulled a handkerchief from his hip pocket and wiped beads of moisture from his forehead.

The old man on the bed breathed weakly, in and out, in and out, and the blankets piled over him rose and fell almost imperceptibly.

At 10:57 Gould stood up fitfully. He peered around the room and saw that there was nowhere left for him to go, and flung himself back into his chair.

It was 10:58. They tensed.

Huber and Braun and Devereaux inched closer to the old man's bed. Branigan and Coszyck tightened their grips on Eleanor Abbott's shoulders. Maunders and Fox braced themselves, leaning towards her as if defying her to seize one of the weapons on the table. Even the five men still seated—Szambel and Carpenter, DiNapoli, Gould, and Ryan—found themselves on the edges of their chairs, ready to spring into action.

But as the clock on the wall ticked loudly and its minute hand crawled closer and closer to the twelve, Eleanor Abbott sat calmly on her high-backed chair, and did not move.

Just before 10:59, Gregory Eliot Abbott's wrinkled eyelids flickered and closed, and his shallow breathing stopped.

"Gentlemen!" Eleanor Abbott's voice shot through the uproar. "If you'll go back to your seats and calm down, I'll explain."

They obeyed her.

She stood by the side of her chair, watching them, her full lips turned slightly upward.

"I warned you," she said. "I told you I was going to kill him, and I did."

"*How?*" Huber demanded.

Her smile broadened.

"Gregory's accident did serious damage to his heart, Mr. Huber, weakened it to a point where it was no longer strong enough to function normally by itself. What's kept it going all year has been medication, a heart stimulant that has to be administered at *very* regular intervals."

Branigan's eyes went wide. She waited, though, until Maunders saw it, and Szambel, and DiNapoli.

"The stimulant," she went on, pointing to the table of weapons, "is in that bottle. It's an incredibly powerful drug, which makes it incredibly dangerous if taken by a person with a normal heart. That's why the bottle is labeled with a skull and crossbones: even a small dose would make a healthy heart speed up so enormously that it could actually burn itself out. But Gregory needed that stimulant to make *his* heart beat normally, and he needed it frequently. He was due for a dose of it at ten minutes past ten this evening. I got up and tried to give it to him, but *you* stopped me."

"You said it was poison!" Coszyck rasped.

"I said no such thing. You *assumed* it was poison, and it *would* have been if *you* had swallowed it—but it was medicine for Gregory, and it was keeping him alive. I tried to give it to him, I tried three times, and each time I tried, you and Inspector Branigan chose to stop me. Without it, Gregory's heart just wasn't strong enough to go on beating, and so he died."

*And so he died,* Branigan thought. *I took the bottle out her hands myself, and so he died.*

The twelve criminologists were silent.

Until, "Well?" Ryan said, his voice thick.

"Well," Eleanor Abbott told them, "you've got two choices. You can arrest me and accuse me of murdering my husband, but I'd like you to stop and think about that for a second. After all, gentlemen, *I* tried to give Gregory his medicine. *You* are the ones who stopped me, and caused his death. If you look at it that way, then *you* killed him, not me. I might get slapped on the wrist for not telling you what was in the bottle an hour ago, but once it gets out that you all sat back and let this happen, you men will be ruined. Your careers will be over."

"She's right," Braun said heavily. "With a story like this, there isn't a jury in the country that could convict her of murder."

"And we'd be sunk," Carpenter added. "I don't think anyone would *dare* to try and make out any kind of a case against us, but the publicity would rip us to pieces. It would destroy us."

The old Fox cleared his throat nervously.

"You said we had *two* possible choices," he reminded her.

"Yes, I did. I've gotten what I wanted, now: a release for Gregory. Is that such a terrible thing to have done? Do you really think he was better off the way he was, in that empty state that medicine and the law agreed was 'alive'? You can turn me in and see where it gets you, gentlemen—or you can work with me, and help me to get away with it."

"You're asking us to help you get away with murder!" Szambel protested.

She held up a hand.

"No, Mr. Szambel, I'm not *asking* you for anything. Arrest me and ruin yourselves, or help to protect me. The choice is entirely yours."

"I can't!" Devereaux cried. "I've spent forty years *upholding* the law. How can I turn around now and make a mockery of it?"

"We've got to," DiNapoli muttered. "She's got us over a barrel. There's no other way out."

"Forget it," Maunders grumbled. "Even if we wanted to, it'd be impossible. We'd never get away with it."

"The twelve of *us?*" Judge Gould chuckled grimly. "Don't be ridiculous! Who'd ever even *think* of challenging us?"

Branigan made the decision for them. "We'll *all* have to discuss it," he said.

She waved a hand at them and turned away.

They gathered in together and talked. Across the room, Eleanor Abbott was unable to make out individual voices or words, but she listened absently, confidently, to the meaningless hum, smiled at explosions of obvious protest, grinned at the eventual murmurs of agreement.

When they finally became silent, she turned to face them.

They were staring at her.

"Gentlemen of the jury," she said, mocking them in her triumph, "have you reached a verdict?"

And Branigan stood up. There was a strange light in his eyes, a light that Eleanor Abbott could not have known, a light that had never been there before.

"We have," he said clearly.

And stopped, waiting.

For a moment she was confused, and then she realized what he wanted and completed the ritual: "How do you find?"

"We find the defendant guilty of murder in the first degree, as charged."

Her smile faded.

"What?" she asked him, not understanding it at first. "What do you mean?"

But when Branigan moved to the table of weapons in the center of the room and picked up the amber bottle and came toward her, she understood. ∾

## THE THREE COFFINS

couple of hours I'll eat that briefcase. You remember, I told you over the phone that Fley had refused to perform and walked out of the theatre last night? Yes. My plain-clothes officer got the story both from the theatre-manager, fellow named Isaacstein, and from an acrobat named O'Rourke, who was friendlier with Fley than anybody else and identified the body later.

"Saturday, naturally, is the big night down Limehouse way. The theatre runs continuous variety from one in the afternoon until eleven at night. Business was booming in the evening, and Fley's first night turn was to begin at eight-fifteen. About five minutes before then, O'Rourke—who had broken his wrist and couldn't go on that night—sneaked down into the cellar for a smoke. They have a coal furnace for hot-water pipes there."

Hadley unfolded a closely written sheet.

"Here is what O'Rourke said, just as Somers took it down and O'Rourke later initialled.

"'The minute I got through the asbestos door and downstairs, I heard a noise like somebody smashing up kindling-wood. Then I did get a jump. The furnace there was open, and there was old Loony with a hatchet in his hand, busting hell out of the last properties he owned and chucking them all in the fire. I said, For cat's sake, Loony, what are you doing? He said, in that queer way of his, I am destroying my equipment, Signor Pagliacci. (I am not sure of the name of Pagliacci, the beggar—and, dingo! in went his fiddle case with the false strings in it.) I was going to tell him he had to go on, but then I said, Loony, great gumbledinky, you can't burn that, it belongs to the house. I mean the cabinet-trick thing he finished with, for you know that turn of his finished—wind it up, he always called like that, the big—when I finished, I said, Loony, you go on in a few minutes, and you'd be together. I said, You go on in a few minutes, and you'd be

## THE MURDER BY MAGIC

dressed.' He said: 'Didn't I tell you? I am going to see my brother. He will do something that will settle an old affair for both of us.'

"Well, he walked over to the stairs and then turned around sharp. It had a queer creepy look with the fire from the furnace shining on it. He said, In case anything happens to me after he has done his business, you will find my brother in the street where I myself live. That is the street where he really resides, but he has taken a room there. Just hear him come old Isaacstein, looking for him. He couldn't behave his ears when he heard Loony refuse to go on. There was a row. Isaacstein bawled 'you know what'll happen if you don't go on?' And Loony says, as pleasant as a threecard man. Yes, I know what will happen.' Then he lifts his hat very courteously, and says, 'Good night, gentlemen. I am going back to my grave.' And up the stairs the lunatic walks, without another word."

Hadley folded up the sheet and replaced it in his brief-case.

"Yes, he was a good showman," said Dr. Fell, struggling to light his pipe. "It seems a pity brother Henri had to . . . what then?"

"Now, it may or may not mean anything to track Henri down in Cagliostro Street, but we're sure to get his temporary hideout." Hadley went on. "The question occurred to me, where was Fley going when he was shot? Where was he walking to? Not to his own room. He lived at number 2B, at the beginning of the street, and he was going in the other direction. When he was shot he was a little over halfway down, near number 18 on his right, and number 21 on his left— in the middle of the street, of course. That's a good trail. Somers out on it. He's to turn out every house, looking for any new or suspicious or oth-

# The Man Who Read John Dickson Carr

WILLIAM BRITTAIN

**A**lthough he did not realize it at the time, Edgar Gault's life first gained purpose and direction when, at the age of twelve, he idly picked up a copy of John Dickson Carr's[1] *The Problem of the Wire Cage* at his neighborhood lending library. That evening after supper he sat down with the book and read until bedtime. Then, smuggling the book into his room, he finished it by flashlight under the sheets.

He returned to the library the following day for another of Carr's books, *The Arabian Nights Murder,* which took him two days to finish—Edgar's governess had confiscated the flashlight. Within a week he read every John Dickson Carr mystery the library had on its shelves. His gloom on the day he finished reading the last one turned to elation when he learned that his favorite author also wrote under the pseudonym of Carter Dickson.

In the course of the next ten years Edgar accompanied Dr. Gideon Fell, Sir Henry Merrivale, et al.[2] through every locked room in the Carr-Dickson repertoire. He was exultant the day his knowledge of an elusive point in high school physics allowed him to solve the mystery of *The Man Who Could Not Shudder* before the author saw fit to give his explanation. It was probably then that Edgar made his momentous decision.

---

1 **John Dickson Carr:** mystery author famous for his impossible-to-solve locked-room mysteries.

2 **Dr. Gideon Fell, Sir Henry Merrivale, et al.:** detectives in Carr's mysteries.

One day he, Edgar Gault, would commit a locked-room murder which would mystify the master himself.

An orphan, Edgar lived with his uncle in a huge rambling house in a remote section of Vermont. The house was not only equipped with a library—that boon to mystery writers, but something few modern houses possess—but the library had barred windows and a two-inch-thick oak door which, opening into the room, could be locked only by placing a ponderous wooden bar into iron carriers bolted solidly to the wall on both sides of the door. There were no secret passages. The room, in short, would have pleased any of Carr's detectives, and it suited Edgar perfectly.

The victim, of course, would be Edgar's Uncle Daniel. Not only was he readily available, but he was a believer in Ralph Waldo Emerson's philosophy of self-reliance,[3] and in order to help Edgar achieve that happy condition, Uncle Daniel had decided to cut the youth out of his will in the near future.

Since Edgar was perfectly prepared to wallow in his uncle's filthy lucre[4] all the days of his life, it was up to him to do the old man in before the will could be changed.

All of which serves only to explain why Edgar, one bright day in early spring, was standing inside the library fireplace, covered with soot and scrubbing the inside of the chimney until it gleamed.

The chimney, of course, was Edgar's means of escape from his locked room. It was just large enough to accommodate his slim body and had an iron ladder which ran up the inside for the convenience of a chimney sweep. The necessity of escape by chimney somewhat disappointed Edgar, since Dr. Gideon Fell had ruled it out during his famous locked-room lecture in *The Three Coffins*. But it was the only exit available, and Edgar had devised a scheme to make use of it that he was sure even John Dickson Carr would approve of. Maybe Edgar would even get a book written about his crime—like Carr's *The Murder of Sir Edmund Godfrey*.

It didn't worry Edgar that he would be immediately suspected of the crime. Nobody saw his preparations—Uncle Daniel was away on business, and the cook and gardener were on vacation. And at the time the crime would actually be committed, Edgar would have two unimpeachable

---

3 **Ralph Waldo Emerson's philosophy of self-reliance:** Emerson taught that people should find their own way in life and not rely on others to pay their way.

4 **filthy lucre:** money.

witnesses to testify that neither he—nor, for that matter, any other human being—could possibly have been the murderer.

Finishing his scrubbing, Edgar carried the pail of water to the kitchen and emptied it down the drain. Then, after a thorough shower to rid his body of soot, he went to the linen closet, took out a newly washed bed-sheet, and returned to the library. Wrapping the sheet around him, he got back into the fireplace and began to climb the iron ladder. Reaching the top, he came down again, purposely rubbing the sheet against the stones at frequent intervals.

Stepping back into the library, he walked to a window, removed the sheet, and held it up to the sunlight. Although wrinkled, it had remained gleamingly white. Edgar smiled as he put the sheet into a hamper. Then, going upstairs, he unlocked the window of a storeroom beside which the chimney rose. After that, in his own room, he dressed in clothing chosen especially for the crime—white shirt, white trousers, and white tennis shoes. Finally, he removed a long cavalry saber from the wall, took it to the library, and stood it in a shadowy corner.

His preparations were nearly complete.

Early that evening, from his chair in the music room, Edgar heard his uncle's return. "Edgar? You home?" The nasal New England twang of Uncle Daniel's voice bespoke two hundred years of unbroken Vermont ancestry.

"I'm in here, Uncle Daniel—in the music room."

"Ayah," said Daniel, looking in though the door. "That's the trouble with you, young fella. You think more o' strummin' that guitar than you do about gettin' ahead in the world. Business first, boy—that's the only ticket for success."

"Why, Uncle, I've been working on a business arrangement most of the day. I just finished about an hour ago."

"Well, I meant what I said about my will, Edgar," Uncle Daniel continued. "In fact, I'm going to talk to Stoper about it tonight when he comes over for cards."

Even the weekly game of bridge, in which Edgar was usually a reluctant fourth to Uncle Daniel, Lemuel Stoper, and Dr. Harold Crowley, was a part of The Plan. Even the perfect crime needs witnesses to its perfection.

Later, as Edgar arranged the last of the three armloads of wood in the library fireplace—and added to the kindling a small jar from his pocket—he heard the heavy knocker of the front door bang three times. He took the opportunity to set his watch. Exactly seven o'clock.

"Take the gentlemen to the music room and make them comfortable," said Uncle Daniel. "Give 'em a drink and get the card table ready. I'll be in presently."

"Why must they always wait for you, Uncle?" asked Edgar, his assumed frown almost a smirk.

"They'll wait forever for me and like it, if that's what I want. They know where the biggest part of their earnings comes from, all right." And still another part of Edgar's plan dropped neatly into place.

Entering the old house, Lemuel Stoper displayed, as always, an attitude of disdain toward everything not directly involved with Uncle Daniel's considerable fortune. "White, white, and more white," he sneered, looking at Edgar's clothing. "You look like a waiter in a restaurant."

"Don't let him get to you, boy," said a voice from outside. "You look fine. Been playin' tennis?" Dr. Crowley, who reminded Edgar of a huge lump of clear gelatin, waddled in and smiled benignly.

"No need to butter the boy up any more," said Stoper. "Dan'l's changin' his will tonight."

"Oh," said Crowley, surprised. "That's too bad, boy—uh—Edgar."

"Yes, Uncle has already spoken to me about his decision," said Edgar. "I'm in complete agreement with it." No sense in providing too much in the way of a motive.

In a small but important change from the usual routine Edgar led the men to the door of the library on the way to the music room. "Uncle," he called. "Dr. Crowley and Mr. Stoper are here."

"I know they're here," growled Daniel. "Wait in the music room. I'll be along in a few minutes."

The two men had seen Uncle Daniel alive and well. Everything was now ready.

In the music room Edgar poured drinks and set up the card table. Then he snapped his fingers and raised his eyebrows—the perfect picture of a man who had just remembered something.

"I must have left the cards upstairs," he said. "I'll go and find them." And before his guests could answer, he left the room.

Once through the door, Edgar's pace quickened. He reached the door of the library eight seconds later. Ignoring his uncle's surprised expression, Edgar took the saber from its corner and strode to the desk where Daniel sat, a newspaper still in his hand.

"Edgar, what in—" Without a word, Edgar thrust the sword violently at his uncle. The point entered Daniel's wattled neck just below the chin and penetrated the neck to the back of the chair, pinning the old man to his place. Edgar chuckled, recalling a similar scene in Carr's *The Bride of Newgate.*

He held the sword in place for several seconds. Then he felt carefully for a pulse. None. The murder had been carried off exactly as planned—in seventy seconds.

Hurrying to the fireplace, Edgar picked up the small jar he had placed there earlier. Then, shuffling his feet through the generous supply of paper among the kindling and wood, he pulled the tall fire screen into place and began to climb up the chimney. Reaching the top, he glanced at his watch. Two minutes had gone by since he had left Stoper and Crowley.

Standing on the roof beside the chimney, Edgar removed several small pieces of blank paper from the jar. He had prepared the paper himself from a formula in a book on World War II sabotage operations. These "calling cards" were designed to burst into flame shortly after being exposed to the air. During the war they had been dropped from planes to start fires in fields of enemy grain. Edgar, who had shortened the time needed to make them ignite, knew the pieces of paper would start a fire in the library fireplace.

Dropping the papers down the chimney, he waited a few seconds, and finally was rewarded with a blast of warm air coming up through the opening. Three minutes and ten seconds. Right on schedule.

Edgar moved along the slanted roof to a large decorative gable in which was set the storeroom window. Carefully inching along the edge of the roof, he raised the window and scrambled inside, taking care not to get dust or dirt on his clothing. He went to his own room, took a fresh deck of cards he had left there earlier, then trotted loudly down the stairs to the music room. He rejoined the two guests a little less than five minutes after he had left them—again, exactly as planned.

Edgar apologized for his short absence, privately gloating over the unsullied whiteness of his clothing. Surely he could not have just climbed up the inside of a chimney from which smoke was now issuing.

Soon Stoper became restless. "I wonder what's keepin' Dan'l?" he grumbled.

"Mebbe we'd better fetch him," said Crowley.

As they rose, Edgar attempted a yawn while his heart pounded wildly. "I believe I'll wait here," he said, trying to act nonchalant.

John Dickson Carr would be proud of me, thought Edgar as Stoper and Crowley left the room. He hoped that the investigation of his crime would not include any theories involving the supernatural. He remembered his disappointment at the ending in *The Burning Court* with its overtones of witchcraft.

Odd, he thought, that there was no shouting, no crashing sounds as the two old men tried to batter down the heavy library door. But there was no need to worry. The plan was perfect, foolproof. It was—

In the doorway of the music room appeared the figure of Lemuel Stoper, looking tired and beaten. In his hand he held a revolver from Uncle Daniel's desk.

"Did his money mean that much to you, boy?" Stoper asked, his voice trembling with shock and rage. "Is that why you did it?"

For only a moment Edgar wondered how Mr. Stoper had got into the library so fast. And then suddenly he knew. For a fleeting instant he wondered if a plea of insanity would help. But then nobody would appreciate the perfect crime he had devised. What would Dr. Fell think of him now? What would H.M. think? What would John Dickson Carr himself think?

What could anyone think of a locked-room murder in which the murderer had forgotten to lock the door? ❧

# RESPONDING TO CLUSTER FOUR

## ESSENTIAL QUESTION: WHY ARE WE FASCINATED BY MYSTERY?

### Thinking Skill SYNTHESIZING

The last group of selections in this book provides an opportunity for independent learning and the application of the critical thinking skill, synthesis. *Synthesizing* means examining all the things you have learned from this book and combining them to form a richer and more meaningful view of the mystery genre.

There are many ways to demonstrate what you know about mystery. Here are some possibilities. Your teacher may provide others.

1. Break into small groups, with each group taking responsibility for teaching a part of the final cluster. To teach the lesson you might:

   a) create discussion questions and lead a discussion

   b) develop vocabulary activities

   c) prepare a test for the cluster selections

   As you develop your activity, keep the essential question in mind:
   "Why are we fascinated by mystery?"

2. Using a selection in this text as a model, write a mystery. Your writing should include some of the qualities of the mystery genre that you have studied. You may work individually or in small groups.

3. Individually or in small groups, develop an independent project that demonstrates your knowledge of the mystery genre. For example, you could research a topic such as forensic medicine and present your findings to the class. Other options might include a music video, dance, poem, performance, drama, or artistic rendering.

# ACKNOWLEDGMENTS

**Text Credits** CONTINUED FROM PAGE 2 "The Dying Detective" from *The Game's Afoot* by Michael and Mollie Hardwick. Copyright © 1969 by Michael and Mollie Hardwick. Reprinted by permission of John Murray (Publishers) Ltd.

"The Framing Game" by Paul Bishop. From *Bad Behavior*, edited by Mary Higgins Clark (Harcourt Brace). Copyright © 1995 by Paul Bishop. Reprinted by permission of Byron Preiss Visual Publications, Inc.

"Invitation to a Murder" by Josh Pachter. Copyright © 1972 by Josh Pachter. First published in *Ellery Queen's Mystery Magazine*. Reprinted by permission of the author.

"Lamb to the Slaughter" from *Someone Like You* by Roald Dahl, published by Michael Joseph. Copyright © 1953 by Roald Dahl. Reprinted by permission of David Higham Associates Ltd.

"The Man Who Read John Dickson Carr" by William E. Brittain. Copyright © 1965 by Davis Publications, Inc. First printed in *Ellery Queen's Mystery Magazine*. Reprinted by permission of the author.

"A Poison That Leaves No Trace" by Sue Grafton. From *The Best of Sisters in Crime*, edited by Marilyn Wallace (Berkley). Copyright © 1990 by Sue Grafton. Reprinted by permission of Aaron Priest Agency for the author.

"Suspense" by Mary Higgins Clark. From *The Crown Crime Companion: The Top 100 Mystery Novels of All Time*, selected by the Mystery Writers of America: annotated by Otto Penzler; compiled by Mickey Friedman (Crown Publishers). Copyright © 1995 by Mystery Writers of America, Inc.

"This Way Nobody Gets The Blame" by Lesley Grant-Adamson. Originally published in 1996 by Severn House in the anthology *Perfectly Criminal*. Copyright © 1996 by Lesley Grant-Adamson. Reprinted by permission of Gregory and Radice as agents for the author.

**Photo and Art Credits** Cover and Title Page: George Tooker, *Voice I*, 1963. Egg tempera on gesso panel, 19 1/2 x 17 1/2 inches. Private Collection. Page 3, 4-5: Courtesy the Minor White Archive, Princeton University. © 1982 by the Trustees of Princeton University, All Rights Reserved. Page 11: Keith Carter, *Giant*, 1997. Page 12: © John Huet, from the book *Soul of the Game* (Melcher Media/Workman Publishing). Pages 24–25: © Graham Harrison. Pages 30, 33, 39: Photographs by Egyptian Expedition, The Metropolitan Museum of Art, NY. Page 34: The Illustrated London News Picture Library. Page 37: The Griffith Institute Ashmolean Museum, Oxford. Page 41: ©1999 C. Herscovici, Brussels/Artists Rights Society (ARS), New York. Courtesy Musées Royaux Des Beaux-Arts De Belgique. Page 42: Wright Morris, *Through the Lace Curtain*, Home Place near Norfolk, Nebraska, 1947. Page 47: René Magritte, *The Eye*, c. 1932-35. Oil on canvas, 23.7 x 23.7 x 5.7 cm. The Art Institute of Chicago. Through prior gift of Arthur Keating, 1989.53. Page 48: George A. Tice, *St. George Diner* from *George A. Tice Photographs: 1953-1973*, copyright © 1975 by George F. Tice. Reprinted by permission of Rutgers University Press. Page 62: Joel Sternfeld, *Tent City, Houston, Texas*, January, 1983. Pages 70-71, 73, 74: Fortean Picture Library. Page 77: Stock Montage. Page 78: The Granger Collection. Page 94: Chicago Historical Society. Page 105: The Courier-Journal. Page 109: Hervé Guibert, *Les Lettres de Matthieu*. Courtesy Galerie Agathe Gaillard, Paris. Page 110: Barry Castle, *Breeding Champions*. Oil/board, 29 x 24 inches, 1977/78. Courtesy Portal Gallery, London. Page 125: David Cunningham. Page 135: Duane Michals, *Ludmilla Tshernina*. Gelatin silver print, 12.3 x 18 cm. Pages 136, 142: William Burlingham.

Every reasonable effort has been made to properly acknowledge ownership of all material used. Any omissions or mistakes are not intentional and, if brought to the publisher's attention, will be corrected in future editions.